Y0-CQL-829

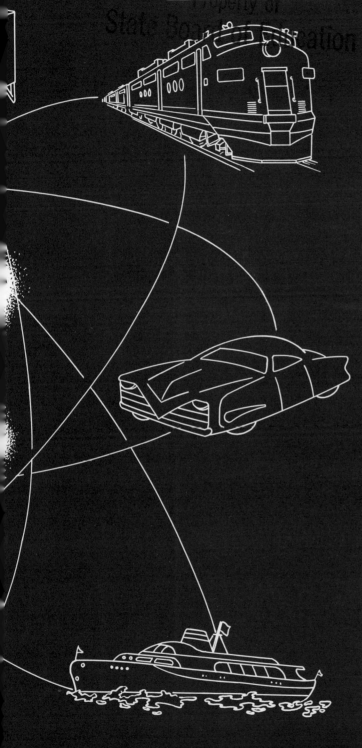

What is Drafting?   1

Occupational Opportunities in Drafting   9

Learning To Draw   17

Making a Layout Drawing   45

Lettering a Drawing   53

Dimensioning a Drawing   65

Making a Working Drawing   75

Drawing Sectional Views   91

Drawing Auxiliary Views   103

Learning about Assembly Drawings and Fasteners   111

How To Make Pattern Drawings   139

Preparation of Pictorial Drawings   155

Drawing Without Instruments   171

Planning a Home   179

Preparing Piping, Heating, and Electrical Drawings   197

Drawing Graphs and Charts   219

Making Prints and Reproductions   229

Supplementary Problems   238

Appendix   253

AMERICAN
TECHNICAL
SOCIETY'S

Drafting

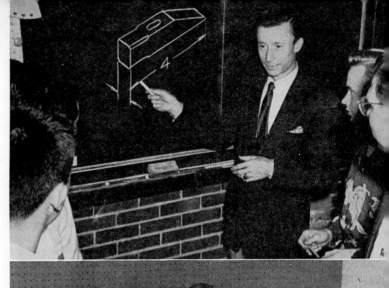

Giachino

Beukema

AMERICAN

TECHNICAL

SOCIETY'S

Drafting

J. W. GIACHINO
Professor of Industrial Education, and Head of Industrial Technology Department, Western Michigan University, Kalamazoo, Michigan

HENRY J. BEUKEMA
Associate Professor of Drafting, Western Michigan University, Kalamazoo, Michigan, and Engineering Checker, Ingersoll Kalamazoo Division, Borg-Warner Corp., Kalamazoo, Michigan

AMERICAN TECHNICAL SOCIETY • CHICAGO, U.S.A.

LIBRARY OF CONGRESS CATALOG CARD NUMBER: 60-7928

FIRST EDITION
1st Printing 1954
2nd Printing 1955
3rd Printing 1957
SECOND EDITION (REVISED)
4th Printing 1960

PRINTED IN THE UNITED STATES OF AMERICA

Table
of
Contents

UNIT 1. What Is Drafting? 1
UNIT 2. Occupational Opportunities in Drafting . . . 9
UNIT 3. Learning To Draw 17
UNIT 4. Making a Layout Drawing 45
UNIT 5. Lettering a Drawing 53
UNIT 6. Dimensioning a Drawing 65
UNIT 7. Making a Working Drawing 75
UNIT 8. Drawing Sectional Views 91
UNIT 9. Drawing Auxiliary Views 103
UNIT 10. Learning About Assembly Drawings and Fasteners 111
UNIT 11. How To Make Pattern Drawings 139
UNIT 12. Preparation of Pictorial Drawings 155
UNIT 13. Drawing Without Instruments 171
UNIT 14. Planning a Home 179
UNIT 15. Preparing Piping, Heating, and Electrical Drawings 197
UNIT 16. Drawing Graphs and Charts 219
UNIT 17. Making Prints and Reproductions 229
Supplementary Problems 238
Design Problems 250
Appendix 253
Index 274

Preface

Since most people must use some basic principles of drafting from time to time, an understanding of this subject is important to everyone. Today we live in an environment where industrial influences dominate the nature of the products we use or the kind of work that provides our livelihood. These influences are especially significant because drafting is the universal medium of communication which makes possible the production of all goods. Actually a day seldom passes when we are not confronted with the problem of having to read or make some kind of a drawing. Thus, we may have to change a tire on the new car, replace a washer in the faucet, assemble a lawn chair, plant a rosebush, build an outdoor fireplace, or read a graph. These and countless other things that are part of our work and play, require a knowledge of drafting principles.

The material in this text is designed to provide an organized plan of instruction for acquiring the essential elements of drafting. Explanations of drafting fundamentals have been kept as simple and brief as possible without unnecessarily sacrificing essential content. Every effort has been made to interpret drafting principles according to the current practices used in industry. Whereas many current drafting texts often include meaningless exercises as vehicles of learning, this text provides a series of realistic and interesting problems that are more conducive to the learning process.

This text will serve as a beginning course for anyone wishing to acquire a basic understanding of drafting. To insure ease of understanding, verbal explanations have been kept at a minimum and supplemented with numerous illustrations. In general, the sequence of instructional units follows a teaching pattern commonly utilized by teachers of drafting.

ACKNOWLEDGMENTS

The authors are extremely grateful to the many individuals who have directly and indirectly participated in the preparation of this text. Specific acknowledgment is made to the following:

Robert Hoffman for producing many of the illustrations.

Students in the Industrial Drafting curriculum at Western Michigan University for preparing drawings and testing the problems.

Neil Schoenhals, Associate Professor of Industrial Arts, Western Michigan University, for his suggestions concerning suitable drawing problems.

To many teachers of Industrial Arts, who while pursuing graduate studies at Western Michigan University, made valuable contributions.

To the various industrial firms who supplied numerous illustrations included in the text.

To the United States Department of Labor for the data included in Unit 2.

J. W. GIACHINO

HENRY J. BEUKEMA

PREFACE TO SECOND EDITION

There will be found in this revised edition, such changes as these:

(1) More extensive treatment of geometric construction.

(2) Separate units with more detailed information on auxiliary and sectional views.

(3) A section on shading added to the unit on pictorial drawing.

(4) Revision of the unit on Schematic Drawing with the material treated under the headings of Piping Drawing, Heating Drawing, and Electrical Drawing.

(5) New problems incorporated in some of the units and supplemental problems for all units placed at the end of the text.

(6) Drafting standards brought up-to-date to conform with recent ASA revisions.

It is believed that these changes as well as other innovations throughout the text will provide wider and richer experiences for the beginning student of drafting.

The authors wish to thank the following organizations for unit heading illustrations:

Morrison Construction Co. for Unit 1; Weber Assoc., Inc. for Unit 14; and Crane Co. for Unit 15.

J. W. GIACHINO

HENRY J. BEUKEMA

Courtesy Kalamazoo Gazette

The draftsman is an important member of the industrial team that designs and produces the essential products, tools and equipment needed by our country.

What Is Drafting?

UNIT 1

Remember that day when you tried to explain to some of your friends the

1. Symbols like these were used by ancient people to tell about the things they did.

Courtesy Allis-Chalmers Manufacturing Co.

way to your home? They could not quite understand your directions. So what did you do? You took a piece of paper and made a little map showing just how they should go. Instead of telling them with words you used a drawing. Drafting is really a process of drawing pictures rather than saying something in words. To be sure, drafting is more precise and exact than the crude sketch you made; nevertheless, it serves the same purpose.

Someone has said, "A picture is worth 10,000 words." When Americans have trouble making themselves understood during their travels in foreign lands, they draw a picture of the thing about which they are inquiring. The foreigner to whom they are talking may not understand our language, but he quickly comprehends the meaning of a picture.

The carvings on the ancient temples of Egypt served to tell a story —a story without words. The natives of our own land used crude pictures and drawings on the walls of caves and on the sides of their wigwams to convey a story of their prowess with bow and arrow. Pictures were understood by everyone in ancient times, even as archaeologists and explorers today know their meaning. See Illustration 1. That is why we say that drafting, or drawing, is a "universal language." It is understood by everyone regardless of race or nationality. It is a language based on the use of a picture rather than on the spoken or written word.

2. For every manufactured product like this television set there are drawings that tell the workmen what to do.

Courtesy Taylor Fibre Co.

Courtesy Lockheed Aircraft Corp

3. Hundreds of drawings were needed to construct this airplane. Before it could be made, each part first had to be drawn.

Why Is Drafting Important?

#2(Drafting is important for many reasons. Without drafting our modern industry could not exist. Were it not for the drawings turned out by the draftsman, our mass production methods of manufacture would be impossible.

If you stop to realize that behind every piece of machinery there is at least one drawing, you begin to see the importance of drafting. ~~See Illustration 3~~. Consider for a moment our new satellites, missiles, battleships, diesel locomotives, automobiles, and electrical appliances, not to mention many others. Each of these is composed of many, many parts. And for every individual part there is a drawing. ~~See Photographs 3, 4, and 5~~. The people who prepare the countless drawings are the industrial draftsmen. These men are skilled in the art of

4. Just imagine the number of drawings that are needed to construct this building. The cooperation of specialists in many fields of drafting is required.

Courtesy American Institute of Steel Construction

5. 4000 engineering drawings and 85000 prints were used in the construction of the Mackinac Bridge, shown above.

making fine, precise, and accurate mechanical drawings from which the workers in the foundries, factories, and laboratories produce the various products.) #2

Who Uses Drawings?

Let us, for example, take any part of an automobile, such as the hub cap, and follow this part from the idea-stage to the final finishing operation.

The automotive designer puts his ideas for the new hub cap in the form of design sketches. These drawings are usually freehand, artistic sketches, and often in color. He submits these sketches to the automotive engineers in charge of the development of the new model. They, in turn, determine how the suggestion for the hub cap can best be incorporated into the overall design of the car, what changes must be made for its production, and what material is to be used in manufacturing it. The final engineering ideas are then given to the draftsman who proceeds to make a finished drawing of the hub cap as shown in Drawing 6. After several processes of revision and checking, copies of the drawing are sent to all the various departments of the factory. For example, the purchasing department will use the drawing to order the material from the suppliers. The toolroom foreman will place the drawing in the hands of experienced toolmakers to construct the tools, jigs, and fixtures necessary to hold and handle the hub cap during the manufacturing operations. The diemakers will use the drawing to make the required dies that will form and shape the thin metal disks into the finished hub caps. The plating department will use the drawing to determine the type of plating which is to go on the hub cap. The foremen and workmen in the various production departments and on the assembly lines must have the drawing to know what operations they are to perform. All of these people not only must have the drawing of the hub cap, but they will need drawings for all the other parts.

Drafting also plays an important part when the new car is introduced to the public. Numerous artists and illustrators will make drawings and sketches for sales brochures and advertisements which will appear in newspapers and magazines. Furthermore, when he purchases the car, the customer will find an operation manual instructing him how to drive and break in the car, when to service it, and other important information, much of which is described by means of drawings. So you see, drawings and sketches follow through the entire industrial process, from the original idea to the actual sale of the automobile to the customer. When any question arises regarding any part of the automobile or its operation, the interested persons look to the drawings for the answers. And so it is in the manufacture of countless other things—drafting is the essential link that makes possible the tools, equipment, appliances, and machinery that we see and use today.

Drafting Helps You Plan

In all of your activities whether they involve play or work a certain amount of planning is necessary. For example, you must plan your study time in order to finish your lessons on schedule. You plan your vacation, your games, your trips. The garden that you plant, the landscaping that you do around the house or the repairs you make, and the things you build, all require planning. If you know something about drafting, it will help you plan more wisely. Most people

6. After the hub cap has been designed, a draftsman prepares a working drawing. A working drawing gives complete information for the manufacture of the part.

Courtesy Chevrolet Motor Division, General Motors Corp.

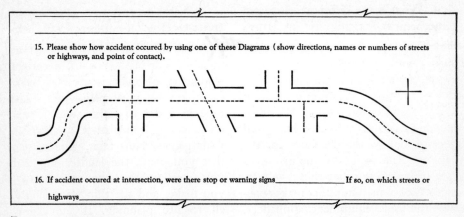

15. Please show how accident occured by using one of these Diagrams (show directions, names or numbers of streets or highways, and point of contact).

16. If accident occured at intersection, were there stop or warning signs_____ If so, on which streets or

highways_____

7. Even when you have an automobile accident, you must use a drawing like this one to show how it happened.

who are good planners try to get their ideas down on paper. If they understand a few basic principles of drafting they can sketch their plans in chart or pictorial form. The result is they are able to visualize better the events in which they intend to participate) #4

Drafting Is Important to Everyone

There are times when almost everyone must make some kind of a sketch or read some kind of a drawing. Remember the electrical fixture #5(which had to be installed in the house and the toy you purchased? You had to follow drawings to assemble them. Why even the wheelbarrow came dis- mantled and you had to use the drawing which illustrated how it had to be put together.

Suppose you wanted to build a simple bookcase, birdhouse, or a flower box. In each case you would first have to make some kind of a drawing. As a matter of fact, when you had that accident with your car you had to sketch out for the insurance company just how the accident happened. See Illustration 7. Without knowing something about drafting you would find it almost impossible to do correctly the many things which you must do from day to day in all of your activities) #5

SELF QUIZ

1. Why is drafting so important in industry?
2. Why is drafting called a univer- sal language? Give some illustrations.
3. To what extent was drawing used by people in ancient times?

4. What is the difference between a mechanical drawing and an artist's sketch?

5. Name several ways in which an understanding of drafting will help you in your play and work.

Courtesy General Dynamics Corp.

8. Many draftsmen were involved in building the atomic submarine Skate, shown above.

PROBLEMS

1. Make a sketch showing the directions one would have to follow in traveling from your home to the ball park.

2. Look through some of your history or geography books and see if you can find pictures of sketches which were made in prehistoric times.

1. How did drafting make possible the manufacture of the items shown in Illustration A?

2. Do these individual pictures represent sketches or finished working drawings?

3. What is the main difference between the illustrations in B and those shown in A?

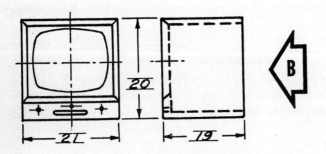

Occupational Opportunities in Drafting

UNIT 2

When you decided to study drafting you probably had a definite reason or goal, but few of us take time to investigate thoroughly all the opportunities. The purpose of this unit is to give you some basic information so you will have a better understanding of the vocational opportunities in drafting.

Fields of Drafting

There are many different classifications of drafting. In general, all drafting may be grouped into five main areas. These are industrial drafting, architectural drafting, designing, topographical drafting, and engineering. The people employed in these different areas must all have special training. Although they may use the same drafting instruments and employ similar drawing techniques, the work of each varies a great deal.

The Industrial Draftsman

Most industrial draftsmen specialize in some particular field of work such as structural, mechanical, aeronautical, electrical, or marine. Their chief responsibility is to make working plans and detailed drawings for products that are to be manufactured. They work from sketches and specifications furnished by an engineer or designer.

A new draftsman usually starts as a tracer or as an apprentice draftsman, and can work himself up to head or chief draftsman. Workers in the higher grade positions are required to make calculations concerning the strength, quality, or cost of materials.

From top drafting jobs, it is possible to advance to design and engineering positions, especially for men who obtain additional training. A person becomes an industrial draftsman by studying at a college, trade or vocational school, or through home-study courses. Some people secure the necessary training by serving a three- or four-year apprenticeship, or by some other type of on-the-job training plus part-time schooling. In any case, the training received should include mathematics, physical science, mechanical drawing, machine shop, and other types of shopwork.

A draftsman must be neat and accurate. He must also have good eye-

1. There are many jobs available in the drafting field.

sight, manual skill, and a talent and liking for drawing in addition to technical knowledge.

The Architect

The architect plans and designs all types of buildings. Many of them specialize in one or more of the major fields of architecture such as private residences, apartments, farm buildings, factories, commercial buildings, institutional and transportation buildings.

Architects who are in private practice serve their clients as professional advisers in a relationship similar to that of doctors and lawyers to their clients. Before designing a building, the architect first consults with the client on the purpose to be served, general style, size, location, cost range, materials, and other characteristics desired. See Photograph 3. In planning the building he takes into consideration economy of layout and construction as well as appearance and efficiency. After preliminary drawings have been made and approved by the client, the architect prepares detailed working plans, specifications, and obtains estimates of cost. See Illustration 4. In addition, he often arranges the contract between the owner and building contractor for the construction of the building, supervises the progress of the work, and certifies to the completion of the building.

Most architects are in business for themselves or are employed by architectural firms. A few work for government agencies, construction contractors, and engineering firms or

Courtesy Convair

2. This illustration shows a typical drafting room in industry. Large industries employ many draftsmen.

teach in colleges and technical schools.

A bachelor's degree from one of the recognized architectural schools is generally a minimum requirement for entrance into this profession. A few people without formal training enter the profession by acquiring many years of experience in architectural offices. However, many trained draftsmen are employed by architects to draw the mechanical, electrical, and structural details.

Designers

Workers in this occupation design the shape of a great variety of products, so they will appeal to consumers and meet their needs. Products de-

signed include automobiles, furniture, machinery, electrical appliances, ash

3. Here you see an architect talking over the plans with his clients.

Courtesy Louis C. Kingscott & Associates

Occupational Opportunities in Drafting **11**

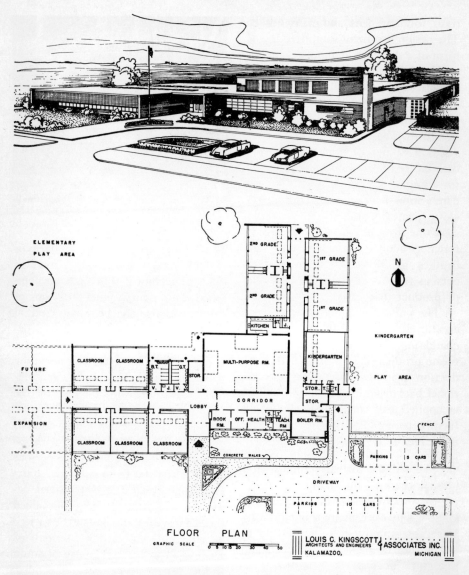

FLOOR PLAN

GRAPHIC SCALE

LOUIS C. KINGSCOTT
ARCHITECTS AND ENGINEERS
KALAMAZOO,

ASSOCIATES INC.
MICHIGAN

ELEMENTARY SCHOOL
FIRST WARD
HASTINGS, MICHIGAN

Courtesy Louis C. Kingscott & Associates

4. This is an example of one type of drawing an architect must prepare. Architects design all kinds of buildings.

trays, fountain pens, and many others. The design is usually submitted in the form of a drawing or model, which is made according to a specific order or request. See Photograph 5.

Industrial design service is frequently rendered by independent design firms. These firms usually employ a group of people who may devote their entire time to designing products for a single large manufacturing company. Some firms render design service to many manufacturers. In either case, one man may design widely different products, ranging from tooth brushes to locomotives. Competent persons transfer easily from one field or product to another.

The industrial designer must have artistic ability, a knowledge of merchandising, and the technical skill to create products suited to modern production methods. A proper educational background, including training in applied arts, the main branches of factory technology, mathematics and other technical subjects, business eco-

5. In this illustration designers are discussing basic requirements for a new design of a fire extinguisher.

6. Here is a group of tool designers making drawings and inspecting special machine fixtures.

nomics, and consumer psychology, is extremely important. A few universities and technical schools have combined these courses into programs of study which may be completed in three or four years and lead to a degree or certificate in industrial design. A number of industrial designers now in practice have had training in architecture, engineering, or one of the sciences.

A less frequent method of entry is through on-the-job training with established designers. Also some persons enter by transfer from industrial drafting, commercial art, commercial designing, engineering, or other allied fields. However, in view of the variety of skills and knowledge essential for success, an integrated course of study at the college level is recommended. Before the beginner can get recognition as a full-fledged designer, he must have created design ideas that have proved successful.

Another classification of designers

are referred to as tool designers. The tool designer originates and prepares sketches of the designs for special fixtures, cutting tools, and other attachments used on machine tools. See Photograph 6. These sketches are made into detailed drawings by draftsmen under the direction of the tool designer. The tool designer must have a practical and detailed knowledge of machine shop practice, drafting, and the characteristics of the materials of which tools and fixtures are made. His duties include developing new tools as well as redesigning and improving tools currently in use. In smaller shops, tool and die makers and machinists often design and make new accessories for machine tools as part of their regular duties. In larger establishments, where many complicated machine-tool accessories have to be designed, special tool designers are employed.

One may qualify as a tool designer in several different ways. Usually, tool and die makers and machinists add to their experience by special training in tool design, drafting, and mathematics, and then advance into tool design work. This move from machine shop and toolroom work to tool design requires not only ability to conceive the idea for a new tool that will fill a definite need in the machining operations but also the knowledge of how to prepare a working design for its construction. Other new entrants qualify by serving a four-year apprenticeship in tool designing, which should include at least two years of machine shop training, plus part-time classes or home-study training. Mechanical engineering graduates who have gained additional practical experience in machine shop work may also enter the field; fewer persons have qualified by this method than by the other two. Occasionally, draftsmen acquire sufficient knowledge of machine shop practice to advance to tool-design work.

Tool designers with engineering degrees are the ones likely to advance to broader and more responsible jobs in tool engineering, which includes the selection, planning, and production of tools as well as designing.

The Topographical Draftsman

The topographical draftsman prepares maps showing portions of the earth's surface. These maps may include land plots, building sites, boundaries of cities, towns, countries; or they may consist of commonly used maps for land, air, or ocean transportation.

The civil engineer generally gathers the data for maps and the drafts-

7. **The tool designer must have experience in machine shop practice.**

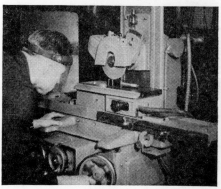

man then lays out the area surveyed. Although the draftsman need not be an engineer, some training in civil engineering is desirable. Mapping through the use of aerial photography is now in wide use by the Air Force and by commercial companies, and they also employ topographical draftsmen. As a rule, most draftsmen employed in this type of work are graduate engineers.

Engineering

Students wishing to enter the engineering profession must acquire an excellent understanding of drafting. This applies to all types of engineering such as mechanical, civil, electrical, industrial, metallurgical, mining, and aeronautical. Along with other technical subjects, each individual enrolled in an engineering program must take several courses in drafting.

Many engineers upon graduation are often employed as draftsmen. Later when they have proved themselves qualified, they move on to more responsible engineering positions.

Courtesy Warren-Knight Co.

8. Here you see a civil engineer carrying out a surveying job. Later the draftsman takes his calculations and makes a drawing.

Military Service

The various branches of the armed forces need skilled draftsmen from most fields. To supply their requirements, all of the services maintain active training programs. A knowledge of drafting is also a decided advantage in every technical specialty. When a person with drafting ability enters military service he has an excellent opportunity for further training and rapid advancement.

SELF QUIZ

1. What are some of the duties of an industrial draftsman?

2. The draftsman generally works from data or sketches supplied by whom?

3. What particular kind of qualifications does an industrial draftsman need to have to qualify for a job?

4. How can a person wishing to become an industrial draftsman prepare himself for this type of work?

5. An architectural draftsman may specialize in what kind of drafting?

6. What kind of training must an architectural draftsman have to qualify for a job?

7. What is the difference between the duties of a designer and those of a draftsman?

8. What is the function of a tool designer?

9. What kind of training must a designer have to be fully qualified?

10. Why must the engineer have a good understanding of drafting?

PROBLEMS

1. Visit a draftsman in your community and find out just what kind of work he does, and what training he has had.

2. Check if there is an employment service in your community. If there is, find out how many draftsmen are employed in your community, what their rate of pay is, and what employment opportunities may exist.

PICTORIAL QUIZ

What field of drafting does each of these illustrations represent?

Learning To Draw

UNIT 3

Whenever you look at a blueprint or drawing of an object, have you ever wondered how a draftsman goes about making it? You probably concluded that he had to use certain types of instruments. This is absolutely correct. As a matter of fact, the draftsman, like any other skilled tradesman, has a special kit of tools which he must use for his particular work. In this unit you will be given an opportunity to learn how to use some of these drafting tools.

Drafting Board

A drawing board 18" x 24" is generally used by most beginners. This board is made of white pine or some other soft wood. It usually consists of several pieces glued together to pre-

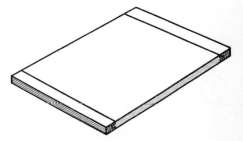

1. This is a typical drafting board used when learning to draw.

vent warping. A cleat is fastened on each end of the board with a tongue-and-groove joint as an additional precaution against warpage. See Illustration 1. Some boards have narrow strips on the underside to provide further rigidity as well as to raise the board slightly from the surface of the drafting table.

The Pencil

There are many different kinds of pencils. Some have hard leads, others have medium or soft leads. The hardness or softness of the lead is designated on the pencil by certain symbols. See Illustration 2.

Thus a pencil marked with a B indicates that the lead is soft. A pencil with the letters HB or F means that the lead is medium-soft, and one marked with H shows that the lead is hard. When a number appears before the letter it simply tells the degree of hardness or softness of the lead. For example, a 4H pencil has a harder lead than a 2H. The grades of pencils run from 6B which have extremely soft leads, to 9H, which have exceptionally hard leads.

The grade of pencil used is governed to some extent by the type of drawing made. Thus a very soft lead is better for sketching, whereas a hard lead is more suitable for fine layouts. Industrial draftsmen generally prefer a medium lead pencil for preparing most detailed drawings because erasing is easier whenever corrections must be made. A hard lead pencil leaves deep

2. The hardness of the lead is shown by a symbol stamped on one end of the pencil.

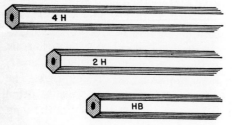

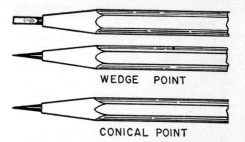

WEDGE POINT

CONICAL POINT

3. Notice how the point of the pencil should be shaped for drafting. Either the conical or wedge point may be used.

impressions or grooves which cannot be removed. It is recommended that at this stage of your training you use an H, 2H, or 3H pencil for most of your drawings. Incidentally, when sharpening your pencil it is a good idea to cut the end that is opposite the symbols. In this way you will always know the grade of pencil you are using.

Sharpening a Pencil for Drawing

To produce clear sharp lines, your pencil will have to be sharpened properly. Two types of points are used for drawing: the conical and wedge (chisel point). See Illustration 3. The conical point is recommended for all-purpose work. Some draftsmen, however, prefer the wedge-shaped point for drawing straight lines and the conical point for lettering and making curved lines. Here is the correct procedure for sharpening a pencil:

1. Sharpen the pencil in a pencil sharpener, and then with a knife uncover about ⅜" of the lead as shown

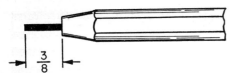

4. To sharpen a pencil correctly, first sharpen it in the pencil sharpener and then slice the wood off until ⅜″ of the lead is exposed.

in Illustration 4. Notice the slight shoulder where the lead is exposed. The advantage of shaping the wooden section in this way is that it permits the lead to be held closer to the T-square and triangle. It also makes possible the repointing of the pencil several times without having to use the sharpener.

2. Roll the pencil on a sandpaper pad or file until the point assumes the shape of a cone. See Illustration 5. If a wedge-shaped point is desired, first roll the point slightly, as in shaping for a cone, and then finish the operation by rubbing both sides of the point flat on the sandpaper.

To simplify the process of sharpening a pencil, many drafting rooms use a special sharpener equipped with

5. After the pencil is sharpened, form the point by rubbing it on a sandpaper pad.

"draftsman's cutters." This cutter removes the wood only, leaving the graphite exposed so that it may be pointed to suit the draftsman's convenience. See Illustration 6. The lead is then pointed by rubbing it on a sandpaper pad or file as previously de-

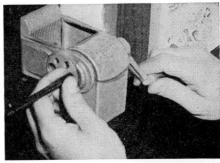

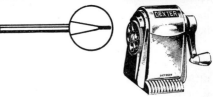

6. This type of pencil sharpener removes the wood only.

scribed or by means of another type of sharpener. The second sharpener points the lead to a conical shape. See Illustration 7.

Measuring Scales

Three types of scales are used in drafting. These are the architect's, the mechanical engineer's, and the civil engineer's scales. The architect's scale is used in making drawings of buildings and other structural parts. The mechanical engineer's scale is often employed by draftsmen for drawing

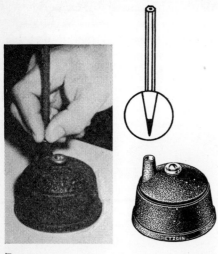

7. This sharpener is used by draftsmen to point lead to a conical shape.

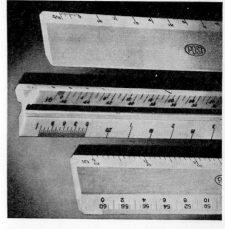

8. The scales shown in this illustration are the ones used by draftsmen. The triangular architect's scale is the most popular for general drawing.

machines and machine parts. The civil engineer's scale is utilized primarily for laying out maps or survey drawings. Each of these scales is available in the triangular or flat shape. See Photograph 8.

Although many draftsmen prefer to use the flat scale, or "stick" as it is often called, the triangular shape is the most popular for school purposes. You will find that the triangular scale has half-round grooves running the full length of the sides. These grooves make it easier to pick up and handle the scale.

A scale guard, as shown in Illustration 9, is often clamped over one of the measuring edges. Since the scale has several different measuring edges, this guard keeps the desired scale in position for instant use.

The Architect's Scale

If you examine the architect's triangular scale, you will find that each edge has a different measuring unit. These units have been designed so the part being drawn can be represented on standard-size paper. Some objects are so large that it is practically impossible to draw them full size. Accordingly, when laying out such objects, they must be reduced in size. Other objects are often too small to draw actual size, and so for clarity

9. Notice how a scale guard is fastened on the scale. This guard keeps the scale in the right position.

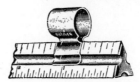

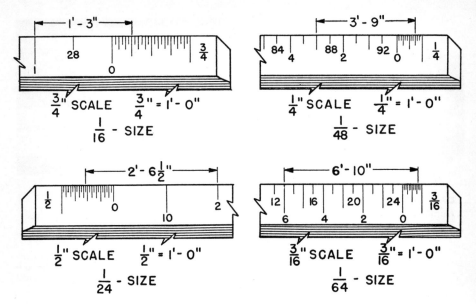

10. The different graduations on the architect's scale permit making any size drawing. Notice how these graduations are marked.

these parts must be drawn larger. The various measuring units on the architect's scale thereby make it possible for the draftsman to produce any size drawing that is required.

You will find that one edge of the architect's scale is divided into inches with subdivisions of sixteenths. The remaining edges are set off in units which represent certain proportions in terms of feet and inches. These measuring units are labeled 3, 1½, 1, ¾, ½, ⅜, ¼, ³⁄₁₆, ³⁄₃₂, and ⅛. Thus, the edge marked with a 3 means that 3″ is equal to one foot. The edge having 1½ means that 1½″ equals one foot, and so on. See Illustration 10.

When the various measuring units are used, a drawing is said to be drawn to scale, such as, full size, half-size,

quarter-size, etc. The scales used most often for full size and reduced drawings are:

Full size—12 in. equals 1 ft. or $1'' = 1''$
¾ size—9 in. equals 1 ft. or $¾'' = 1''$
½ size—6 in. equals 1 ft. or $½'' = 1''$
¼ size—3 in. equals 1 ft. or $¼'' = 1''$
⅛ size—1½ in. equals 1 ft. or $⅛'' = 1''$
¹⁄₁₂ size—1 in. equals 1 ft. or $1'' = 12''$
¹⁄₁₆ size—¾ in. equals 1 ft.
¹⁄₂₄ size—½ in. equals 1 ft.
¹⁄₄₈ size—¼ in. equals 1 ft.

Whenever a drawing of an object has to be enlarged, then these same measuring units can be made to represent inches instead of feet. For example, suppose you wanted to draw a part several times larger than its actual size. You might use the scale marked

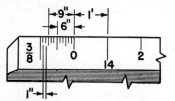

11. The scale on the end divides feet into inches. (The zigzag lines indicate that only a part of the object is shown.)

with 3. Now in this case instead of the 3 representing units in which 3″ equals one foot, the scale can be used so each division represents one inch. This produces a drawing that is three times the actual size of the object. Similarly, the other scales may be used for the same purpose.

represent inches and fractions of an inch. See Illustration 11. The small scale at the end simply takes a large division and subdivides it into smaller units to make it possible to lay off distances that are given in fractional parts of a foot such as 1′-6″, 1′-9″, etc.

To use another illustration—assume that you want to make a drawing ¼ size. First determine the largest unit that is to be laid off, such as 2′-6″. The unit 2′, then, is the largest foot-dimension. Locate the scale marked 3, which is the ¼ scale, and on it find the 2′ division mark. Then reading back from the 0 into the smaller unit scale on the end, find the 6″ mark. From this point to the 2′ division will be our

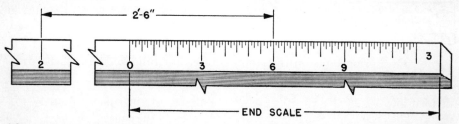

12. Here is how you locate a dimension on the scale. Remember the fractional units are found on the end scale.

Drawing an Object to Scale

Let us assume that you wish to draw an object which must be reduced in size. Suppose, for example, that your drawing paper is such that you can conveniently lay out the object to a scale of ⅜″ = 1′-0″. Find the scale that is marked ⅜. Remember that each division line on this scale represents one foot. Observe, too, that on the end of the scale the divisions are divided into smaller units. These smaller units

dimension to be marked off on the paper. See Illustration 12.

The Mechanical Engineer's Scale

The mechanical engineer's scale has measuring units that are similar to

13. Here is a sample of the mechanical engineer's scale.

Courtesy Eugene Dietzgen Co.

those of the architect's scale. The only difference is that the measuring edges are limited to drawing objects that will be ⅛, ¼, ½, and full size. The units on each scale represent inches and fractional parts of inches. Thus, to draw an object to a ¼ scale, the measuring edge marked ¼ would be used. Each main division on this scale then would be equal to one inch. The fractional part of the inch is indicated by the small division lines. See Illustration 13.

The Civil Engineer's Scale

The civil engineer's scale is graduated in units to represent decimals. Each one-inch unit on the scale is

Courtesy Eugene Dietzgen Co.

14. The graduations on the civil engineer's scale represent decimal units.

divided into 10, 20, 30, 40, 50, and 60 parts. The edge marked 10 simply means that one inch has been subdivided into 10 equal parts, the edge marked 20 has each inch divided into 20 parts, and so on with the other measuring edges. See Illustration 14.

15. Horizontal lines are drawn with the aid of a T-square.

Courtesy Frederick Post Co.

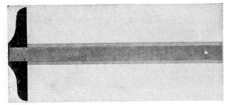

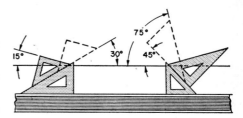

16. Slanted lines are drawn with the aid of 45- and 30-60-degree triangles. By combining these triangles, lines can be drawn at various angles.

As a matter of fact, these parts can be used to represent any desired measuring units such as inches, feet, or miles. Suppose you wanted to lay off 2.125″. With the measuring edge labeled 10, locate the second large division marked 2 plus 1¼ subdivisions. If the same dimension is to be set off in half size, the scale marked 20 is used.

T-Square and Triangles

The instrument used for drawing horizontal lines is known as a T-square. See Photograph 15. Slanting lines are drawn with triangles resting on the T-square. The two triangles used by the draftsman are called the 45-degree and the 30-60-degree triangle. By combining these two triangles, various other angles can be found. See Illustration 16.

Drawing Horizontal, Vertical, and Slanted Lines

1. Mark off the location where the line is to be drawn by placing the scale on the paper and making a small mark with the point of the pencil next to the graduation on the scale. See Illustra-

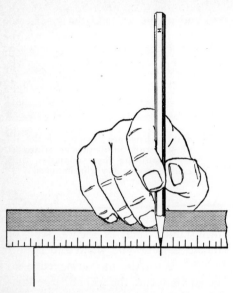

17. To draw lines, first make a light mark next to the graduation desired.

19. To draw vertical lines, move the pencil along the edge of the triangle from the bottom to the top.

tion 17. When making the mark, twirl the point of the pencil.

2. *To draw a horizontal line,* place the T-square on the board with the head of the T-square resting firmly against the edge of the board. Locate

18. To draw a horizontal line, move the pencil along the edge of the T-square from left to right.

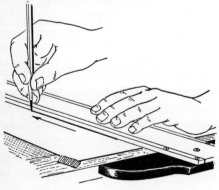

the pencil on the mark and move the T-square up to the pencil. Now draw the line moving the pencil from left to right. Tilt the pencil in the direction the line is being drawn and slightly away from the edge of the T-square. See Illustration 18. Use a uniform pressure on the pencil and roll it slightly as the line is drawn.

3. *To draw vertical lines,* rest the triangle against the T-square. Slide the triangle up to the pencil point and draw the line by starting at the bottom and running the pencil toward the top of the paper while holding it slightly away from the edge of the triangle. Hold the T-square and triangle firmly as shown in Illustration 19.

4. *To draw slanted lines,* place the triangle with the angle required against the edge of the T-square. Slide the triangle up to the pencil point and draw the line. Check Illustration 20, for the direction in which the pencil is to move. You will note that if the line is to be drawn in position *X,* the pencil runs from the top of the triangle to the bottom. If the line is to be

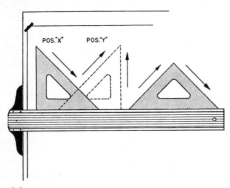

20. Notice the direction the pencil should move when drawing slanted lines with the aid of triangles.

drawn in position *Y*, the pencil should be moved from the bottom of the triangle to the top.

Drawing Angular Lines with a Protractor

Sometimes you will have to draw slanted lines at an angle which cannot be obtained with a triangle. In this case, a protractor will have to be used. You will notice in Illustration 21 that a protractor is a semicircular form divided into units called degrees. Two scales are shown on the protractor with each scale having units running from 0 to 180 degrees. The outer scale is used for drawing angular lines that

21. To locate the angle of some types of slanted lines a protractor like this must be used.

Courtesy Eugene Dietzgen Co.

extend to the left and the inner scale for lines that must be drawn to the right. This is how a protractor is used:

1. Place the protractor on the T-square as shown in Illustration 22 with its center point on the mark where the line is to be drawn.

2. Find the desired angle on the protractor, using either the inner or outer scale, and mark it with a point.

22. To use a protractor first place it on the T-square and mark the desired angle as shown in this illustration.

3. Remove the protractor and, with the edge of a triangle or straightedge, draw a line connecting the two points. See Illustration 23.

Drawing Circles and Arcs with a Compass

Circles and parts of circles, or *arcs*, are drawn with a compass. The large compass is used to draw circles whose radii range from 1 to 6 inches. (The *radius* of a circle is the distance from the center to the outside.) For very small circles or arcs, the bow compass is used. See Photograph 24. This is how you should proceed to draw circles and arcs using these instruments:

1. Shape the lead in the compass to a bevel point as shown in Illustration 25.

2. Adjust the point on the compass so it is slightly longer than the lead. Then set the compass to the required radius.

3. Hold the compass as shown in Illustration 26 and revolve it to the right. Tilt the compass in the direction the circle is being drawn. Exert only enough pressure on the compass to keep the point from coming out of the paper.

4. To draw circles that are larger

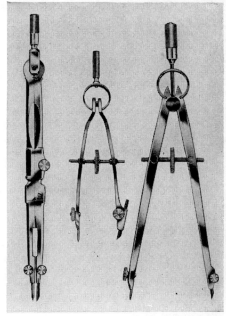

24. Circles and arcs are drawn with a compass.

than 3″ in diameter, better results will be obtained if you bend the legs of the compass at the joints so they will be perpendicular to the paper.

5. To draw circles having a larger radius than 5½″, insert the lengthen-

23. After the desired angle is marked, remove the protractor and draw a line connecting the two points laid out.

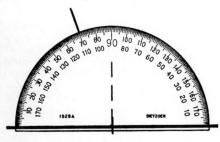

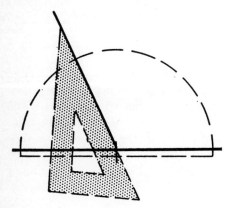

25. To use a compass, first shape the lead to a bevel point like this.

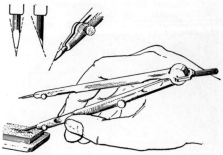

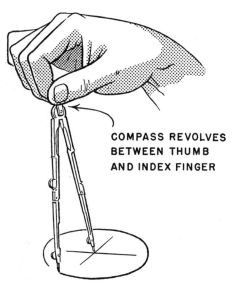

COMPASS REVOLVES
BETWEEN THUMB
AND INDEX FINGER

26. Hold the compass like this to draw a circle or arc.

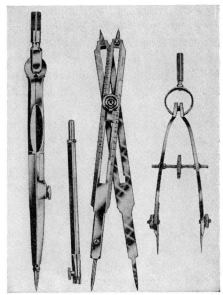

Courtesy Frederick Post Co.

28. Dividers like these are used to lay out equal spaces.

ing bar in the compass. Hold the compass with two hands as shown in Illustration 27 and draw the circle.

Dividers

Dividers are used to space off equal distances, to divide lines into equal parts, and to transfer dimensions. This instrument resembles the compass ex-

27. This is how large circles can be drawn with the aid of a lengthening bar.

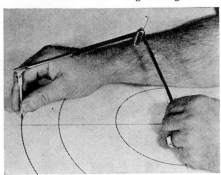

29. This is how dividers should be held and used.

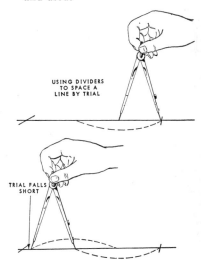

USING DIVIDERS
TO SPACE A
LINE BY TRIAL

TRIAL FALLS
SHORT

cept that the legs are equipped with two sharp points. The plain dividers are used for large measurements and the bow dividers are used when working with small spaces. See Photograph 28. Here is how dividers are used:

1. *To space off equal distances*, set the points of the dividers to the required length. Hold the dividers as shown in Illustration 29 and set off the spaces by rotating the dividers between the thumb and finger. Rotate the dividers first on one side of the line and then on the other side of the line.

2. *To divide a line* into equal parts, first determine the number of equal distances that are required. Set the dividers to an approximate distance and space off the parts. If the dividers fall

30. Irregular curves are drawn with these French or Ship curves. There are curves designed for many purposes.

Courtesy Eugene Dietzgen Co.

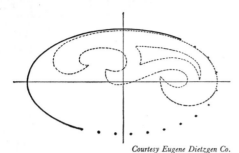

31. To draw an irregular curve, lay out a series of points to indicate the desired curve and then fit the French or Ship curve to line up with these points.

short of or beyond the given line, lengthen or shorten the dividers and repeat the operation.

3. *To transfer a distance* from one part of the drawing to another, simply adjust the dividers to the required space and then press the points lightly on the paper in the new position.

Drawing Irregular Curved Lines

Irregular curves are usually drawn with a French curve or a Ship curve. French curves combine many short curves; Ship curves provide long gradual curves. See Illustration 30. These curves are available in numerous shapes and sizes. They are made either of metal, transparent celluloid, or plastic. Here is how they should be used:

1. Lay out a series of points to indicate the shape of the curve.

2. Locate a part of the curve that fits as many points as possible and scribe a line. See Illustration 31.

3. Move the curve to its next position and draw a line to connect with the first scribed line. Continue this procedure until the curved line is completed. Be careful to have the line flow smoothly so that the points where the curved sections are joined will be uniform with the rest of the line.

Drafting Templates

A variety of templates have been designed to simplify the job of the draftsman and to minimize many tedious and time-consuming operations. One of the most common is the *Draft-*

32. This hole template is used to draw small circles, arcs, screw threads and nuts. This device speeds the draftsman's work.

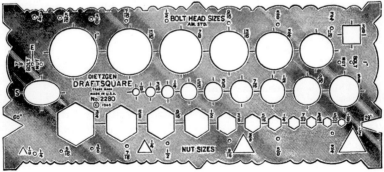

Learning To Draw 29

square or *hole template*. See Illustration 32. This template is used to draw small circles and arcs, screw threads, and nuts.

To draw a side view of a nut, first lay out the limits of the nut, then locate the nut head outline by size on the edge of the template. Position the template and trace in the required shape, as in Illustration 33.

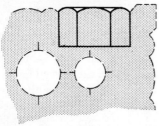

33. This is how a template is used to draw a nut.

To draw a small circle, lay out the center lines of the circle. Place the template so the quadrant lines of the required circle coincide with the center lines drawn on paper and trace the circle. Illustration 34 shows how.

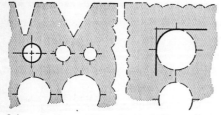

34. (Left) This is how a template is used to draw a circle.
35. (Right) This is how a template is used to draw an arc.

To draw an arc, lay out the tangent lines. Set the template so the quadrant lines of the correct size radius coincide

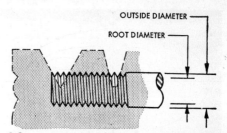

OUTSIDE DIAMETER
ROOT DIAMETER

36. This is how a template is used to draw screw threads.

with the tangent lines and trace the arc. See Illustration 35.

To lay out screw threads, first construct the lines to represent the outside and root diameters. Place the template as shown in Illustration 36 and draw the connecting lines.

Drafting Machine

The drafting machine is a device used extensively by draftsmen. It replaces the T-square, scale, triangle, and protractor. The machine, as you will see in Photograph 37, consists of two movable arms or links which make it possible to locate the horizontal and vertical straightedges at any desired position. A controlling or index head allows the scale or straightedge to be set at any angle.

Drawing Paper

The early practice in drafting was to make all penciled drawings on cream, buff, or green drawing paper. Tracing paper or tracing cloth was then placed over the drawing and traced in pencil or ink. Today industrial draftsmen make all pencil drawings directly on tracing paper (vellum) or on pencil tracing cloth.

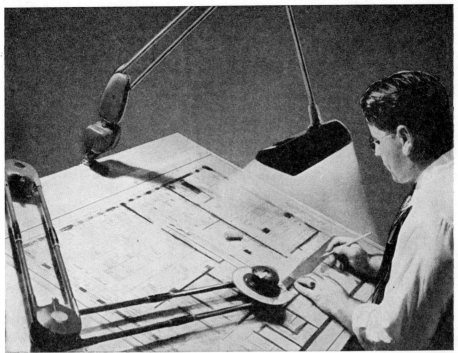

<small>*Courtesy Frederick Post Co.*</small>

37. **Many draftsmen use this drafting machine. Notice that this machine eliminates the regular T-square, scale, triangles, and protractor.**

Blueprints or other types of prints are then produced from these tracings.

Drawing or tracing paper is available in large rolls and in sheet form. The following are recognized as standard-size sheets:

A-size—8½" x 11" or 9" x 12"
B-size—11" x 17" or 12" x 18"
C-size—17" x 22" or 18" x 24"
D-size—22" x 34" or 24" x 36"
E-size—34" x 44" or 36" x 48"

Alphabet of Drawing Lines

Various types of lines have been adopted to describe the shape and size of an object. This alphabet of lines is given in Illustration 38, on page 32.

The meaning of these lines is indicated by their weight and construction. You will notice in Illustration 38 that three weights of lines are used—heavy, medium, and light. Remember that contrast in weight of lines should be obtained not by degrees of darkness, but by differences in thickness.

When making a drawing, it is important to keep all lines clean and sharp. They should meet squarely at corners and blend smoothly at all points of contact. As soon as a line begins to vary in thickness, resharpen the lead.

<small>*Learning To Draw* **31**</small>

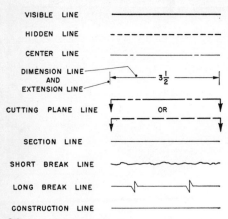

VISIBLE LINE	———————————
HIDDEN LINE	– – – – – – – – –
CENTER LINE	— — —————— — —
DIMENSION LINE AND EXTENSION LINE	⊢———— $3\frac{1}{2}$ ————⊣
CUTTING PLANE LINE	— — — OR — — —
SECTION LINE	———————————
SHORT BREAK LINE	∿∿∿∿∿
LONG BREAK LINE	——/\———/\——
CONSTRUCTION LINE	———————————

38. In making a drawing, these lines will have to be used.

Description of Drawing Lines (See Illustrations 38 and 39)

A visible line is a heavy line used to outline the exterior contour of the object.

A hidden line is a medium weight line used to describe edges which are not visible to the eye. This line is slightly narrower than the object line.

Dimension and extension lines are very thin solid lines. The dimension line is used to designate the size of the part drawn. Numerals are inserted in the middle of this line to show length, width, or thickness. Extension lines are drawn from the object to the terminal points of the dimension line.

Center lines are thin broken lines used to indicate the axes of all symmetrical views. They are usually the first lines drawn and serve as reference lines for dimensions.

A break line is a medium weight, freehand, zigzag line used to break an object when it is too large to get on the drawing paper.

A cutting plane line is a heavy broken line drawn across an object to show a sectional view. The arrowheads on the ends of the line indicate the direction in which the section is to be seen. A sectional view is used to describe the interior construction of the object.

Section lines are very thin parallel lines drawn not less than $\frac{1}{16}''$ apart through the area cut by the cutting plane in the sectional view. These lines

39. Notice how the alphabet of lines is used for a drawing. Each line has a meaning for the person who knows drafting.

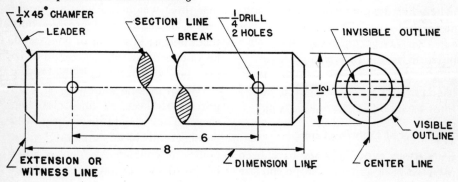

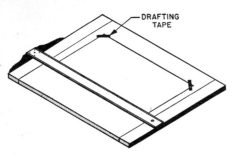

40. Fasten the paper on the board with strips of drafting tape.

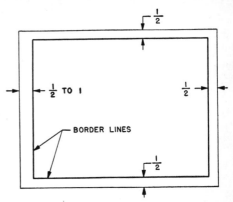

41. A border line is drawn near the edge of the paper to limit the working space.

are usually made at some appropriate angle such as 30°, 45°, or 60°, depending upon the particular nature of the sectional view.

Construction lines are very light lines which are used as a guide to block in the object, or as a base for drawing permanent dark lines later. They should be very light so that no erasing is necessary.

The lines described above are the alphabet of drafting; they must be mastered as thoroughly as the alphabet of a language.

How To Lay Out a Drawing Sheet

1. *Fasten the paper to the drawing board.* Place the paper so it is approximately 2 or 3 inches from the top edge of the board and about the same distance in from the left edge of the board. Fasten a strip of drafting tape, about 1″ long, across the upper left-hand corner of the drawing paper. See Illustration 40. Slide the T-square up to the bottom edge of the paper. When the edge of the paper is even with the top edge of the T-square, place another strip of tape on the up-

per right-hand corner. Then remove the T-square and place strips of tape across the bottom corners.

2. *Draw border lines around the paper.* Border lines are used to improve the appearance of the drawing and to limit the space for laying out views of the object to be drawn. No definite rule can be given for the location of border lines from the outside edges of the paper. These distances may vary from ½″ to 1″ or more. See Illustration 41. Unless your teacher has instructed you otherwise use this layout. The border lines are usually drawn in lightly and darkened only after the entire drawing is completed. This procedure prevents the lines from smudging as the drawing is being worked on.

3. *Draw a title strip.* All drawings have a space in the lower right-hand corner or across the bottom of the sheet to record certain data. This space is frequently referred to as the title

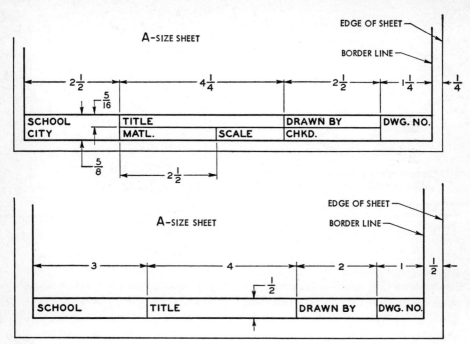

42A. Titles may be arranged this way. In laying out a title, always make a pleasing, balanced arrangement.

block, or title strip. The title strip should provide spaces for information such as name of the object, scale, name of the school, name of the student, date of completion, number of the sheet, and initials of the person who checked the drawing. Since title strips vary in size, no specific dimensions for laying them out can be given. Consult your instructor for the correct dimensions. See Illustrations 42A and 42B which provide several suggestions which may be used if they are found suitable.

How To Erase Pencil Marks

Very often you will need to remove certain pencil marks from the paper. Most of these marks or lines can be eliminated with ordinary pencil erasers. For best results, this is how you should proceed:

1. Remove all the instruments from the drawing board.

2. Clean the eraser by rubbing it on a piece of paper.

3. Place the fingers of the left hand near the mark that is to be erased. Rub the eraser back and forth. Be sure to hold the paper firmly; otherwise it may wrinkle or tear as you rub it. Rub slowly, without too much pressure, so the eraser will not overheat and leave a stain on the drawing.

4. If you must erase near other lines which you do not want removed,

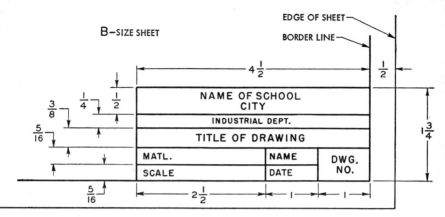

B—SIZE SHEET

EDGE OF SHEET

BORDER LINE

$4\frac{1}{2}$ $\frac{1}{2}$

$\frac{3}{8}$ $\frac{1}{4}$ $\frac{1}{2}$

$\frac{5}{16}$

$1\frac{3}{4}$

NAME OF SCHOOL CITY		
INDUSTRIAL DEPT.		
TITLE OF DRAWING		
MATL.	NAME	DWG. NO.
SCALE	DATE	

$\frac{5}{16}$ $2\frac{1}{2}$ 1   1

42B. Here is another type of title strip. Every industry uses a standardized title form that is suited to its requirements.

use an erasing shield as shown in Illustrations 43A and 43B. Select an opening in the shield that best fits the mark to be removed. Hold the shield firmly over the pencil mark, and proceed to erase through the opening. If a shield is not available, the same results can be obtained by covering the area not to be touched with a piece of stiff paper.

5. When the erasing is completed, wipe off the paper with a clean cloth or brush and touch up any of the lines

that might have been damaged during the erasing process. To help keep a drawing clean, draftsmen often sprinkle granulated rubber over the paper. These small particles act as bearing surfaces which keep the T-square and triangles from actually touching the paper. As a result, dirt and pencil graphite are prevented from spreading over the drawing.

43B. This is how to use the erasing shield. With a shield, neat erasures can be made.

43A. This shield is very helpful when it is necessary to erase.

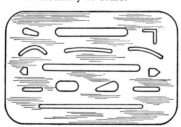

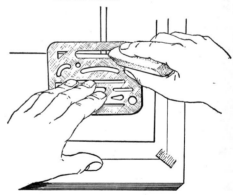

In the process of making a drawing there will be occasions when you will need to use certain types of geometric constructions, such as bisecting a line or an arc, or drawing lines and arcs tangent to each other. Although the experienced draftsman uses a great many of these constructions, you will need only the following basic ones at this time.

To Bisect a Line (See Construction 44)

1. To find the center of any given line such as *AB*, set the compass for any radius greater than one-half of *AB*. Using *A* and *B* as centers, draw two arcs to intersect at *C*, and two arcs to intersect at *D*.

2. Draw a straight line to connect points *CD*. The point where line *CD* crosses *AB* is the center of the line.

3. Another method that may be used to bisect a line is with a triangle and T-square. See Construction 45. Place any triangle on the T-square and draw lines *AC* and *BC* so they will intersect. Slide the triangle up to point *C* and draw a vertical line.

To Bisect an Arc (See Construction 46)

1. To bisect arc *AB*, set the compass at a radius greater than one-half of *AB*. With *A* and *B* as centers, draw two arcs intersecting at *D* and two arcs intersecting at *E*.

2. Draw a line connecting points *D* and *E*. The point *C* where line *DE* crosses the arc represents the center of the given arc.

To Divide a Line into Equal Parts (See Construction 47)

1. Suppose you want to divide a given line into a number of equal parts such as eight. First draw line *AB*, which is the line to be divided.

2. Now draw line *CB* at any angle with *AB*. Starting at *B* on line *CB*, lay

44. One way a line can be bisected. 45. How a line can be bisected with a triangle and T-square. 46. How an arc can be bisected. 47. How a line can be divided into any number of equal parts.

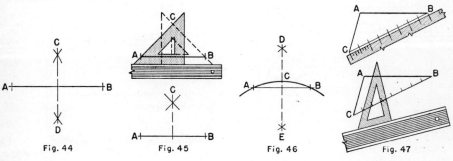

Fig. 44   Fig. 45   Fig. 46   Fig. 47

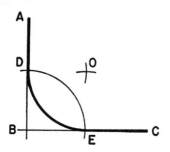

48. This is how to draw an arc tangent to two lines at 90°.

off eight equal spaces either with dividers or a scale as illustrated.

3. From the point where the last space falls (*C*), draw a line connecting *C* with *A*. Then with a triangle, set parallel with line *AC*, draw lines from the points on line *CB* to line *AB*. The division points will be where the parallel lines intersect on line *AB*.

To Draw an Arc Tangent to Two Lines at 90° (See Construction 48)

1. Quite often you will need to draw an arc tangent to two lines as shown in Construction 48. Draw the

two lines *AB* and *CB* so they intersect at *B*.

2. Set the compass to the given radius and, with *B* as a center, draw an arc cutting a line *AB* at *D* and line *CB* at *E*.

3. Then using the same radius and with *D* and *E* as centers, draw two arcs to intersect at *O*.

4. With *O* as a center and with the compass set at the same radius, draw the arc tangent to lines *AB* and *CB*.

To Draw an Arc Tangent to Two Lines Not at 90° (See Construction 49)

1. When an arc must be drawn to two given lines making an angle of more or less than 90°, set the compass at the given radius *OR* and using any points on lines *AB* and *BC*, draw a series of arcs.

2. Draw straight lines tangent to these arcs to form lines parallel to *AB* and *BC* and extend them to intersect at *O*.

3. With *O* as a center and the compass set at the given radius, draw the arc to lines *AB* and *BC*.

To Bisect an Angle (See Construction 50)

1. To bisect an angle, use point *A* as a center and with the compass set at any convenient radius, draw an arc cutting line *AB* at *D* and line *AC* at *E*.

2. Set the compass at a radius greater than one-half of *DE*. With *D* and *E* as centers, draw two arcs to intersect at *O*.

49. This is how to draw an arc tangent to two lines not at 90°.

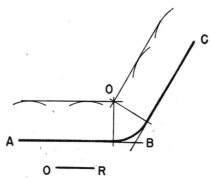

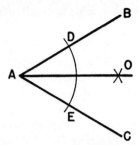

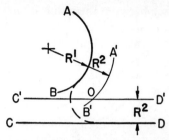

50. This is how an angle is bisected.

3. Draw a line from O to A. The line OA bisects the angle.

To Draw an Arc Tangent to a Straight Line and an Arc (See Construction 51)

1. When it is necessary to draw an arc tangent to a straight line and an arc, as shown in Construction 51, set the compass to the given radius R^1 and draw arc AB.

2. Set the compass a distance equal to R^1 plus the specified connecting arc R^2 and draw arc $A'B'$.

3. Draw line $C'D'$ parallel to line CD and to intersect arc $A'B'$ at O. Line $C'D'$ must be a distance equal to R^2 from line CD.

4. With O as a center and the compass set at the given radius R^2, draw the arc tangent to arc AB and line CD.

To Draw Tangent Arcs (See Construction 52)

1. Whenever an object has a series of adjoining arcs as shown in Construction 52, set the compass to R^1 and draw arc AB.

2. Set the compass to R^1 plus R^2 and draw arc $A'B'$.

51. This is how to draw an arc tangent to a straight line and an arc.

3. With the compass set at R^3, draw arc CD.

4. Set the compass at a distance equal to R^3 plus R^2 and draw arc $C'D'$ to intersect arc $A'B'$ at O.

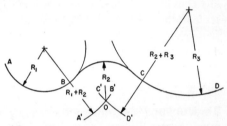

52. This is how to draw tangent arcs.

5. With O as a center and the compass set a distance equal to R^2, draw the arc tangent to arcs AB and CD.

To Draw a Straight Line Tangent to Two Arcs (See Construction 53)

1. To connect arc AB and arc CD with a straight line, first find the dif-

53. This is how a straight line is drawn tangent to two arcs.

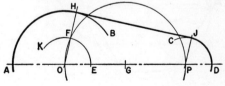

ference between the radius of arcs *AB* and *CD*. Lay off this difference *OE* on the straight line connecting the centers of arcs *AB* and *CD*. With *O* as a center and *OE* as a radius, draw the arc *KE*.

2. Now find the center of line *OP*. Then with *OG* as a radius and *G* as a center, draw arc *OP*, cutting arc *KE* at *F*.

3. Draw a line through points *O* and *F*, cutting arc *AB* at *H*. Now *H* becomes the point of tangency of arc *AB*.

4. Draw line *PJ* parallel with line *OH*. *J* is the point of tangency of arc *CD*.

5. Draw line *HJ*, which is the required tangent to the two arcs.

ADDITIONAL DRAWING CONSTRUCTIONS

To Draw a Regular Hexagon with Given Distance Across Corners (See Construction 1)

1. Draw a circle with AB as the given diameter.
2. Using A and B as centers and with the same radius as the circle, draw arcs to intersect the circle.
3. Draw the sides of the hexagon by joining the points located.

To Draw a Hexagon When the Distance Across Flats Is Given (See Construction 2)

1. Draw a circle having a diameter equal to the distance across the flats.
2. With a 30°–60° triangle and a T-square draw lines tangent to the circle. The connecting points of the tangent lines will provide the true hexagon.

To Draw a Regular Pentagon (See Construction 3)

1. Draw a circle with AB as the given diameter.
2. Draw radius CD perpendicular to the horizontal centerline of the circle.
3. Bisect CB and with the point E as a center and a radius ED, draw arc FC.
4. Using D as a center and with radius DF, draw arc FG. DG will now be one side of the pentagon.
5. With DG as the common chord, mark off the remaining points on the circle.
6. Complete the pentagon by connecting the located points.

1 (left). How a hexagon is drawn when the distance across corners is given. 2 (center). How a hexagon is drawn when the distance across flats is given. 3 (right). How to draw a regular pentagon.

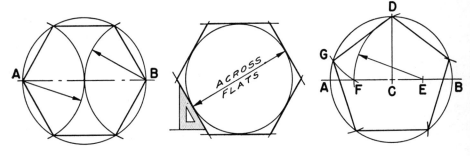

To Draw an Ellipse by Concentric Circle Method (See Construction 4 —½ of the ellipse shown)

1. Given ½ of the major and minor axes CA and CB.
2. Using C as a center, and CA and CB as radii, draw circle arcs.
3. Divide either the large or small circle arc into any number of equal parts and through these division points construct radial lines CD, CE, CF, etc., to intersect both circle arcs.
4. From points D, E, F, etc., draw horizontal lines to intersect vertical lines from points d, e, f, etc. The intersection of these lines will form the points for the ellipse.

5. Connect the points by using an irregular curve.

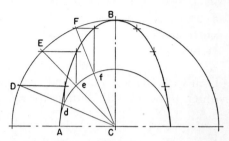

4. This is the construction used in drawing an ellipse by the concentric-circle method.

SELF QUIZ

1. What kind of pencil should you use for drawing?

2. Which pencil has a harder point—one marked 2H or 4H?

3. What is meant by drawing an object to scale?

4. When a scale is marked ¾, what are the values of the divisions on this scale?

5. Suppose you wanted to increase the size of the object which you are to draw three times its actual size, what scale would you use?

6. What is the function of the small units at the end of each scale?

7. What is the difference between a civil engineer's scale and a mechanical engineer's scale?

8. When drawing horizontal lines, in which direction should the pencil move?

9. In which direction should the pencil move when drawing vertical lines?

10. What devices may be used for drawing slanted or angular lines?

11. What is the function of an extension line?

12. When are construction lines used?

PROBLEMS

1. Lay out to any scale, the shape of the head of a T-square similar to the one shown in Illustration 54. Secure actual T-square sizes.

2. Lay out a six-sided Star in a circle having a diameter of 6″, as shown in Drawing 55. Use full scale. Make outlines black. Erase all construction lines.

3. Lay out the Insigne shown in

Drawing 56 according to the sizes shown. Use a scale of $1'' = 1'$. Lightly shade the colored areas.

4. Make a layout drawing of the sail for the Optimist-Pram shown in Drawing 57. Use any desired scale.

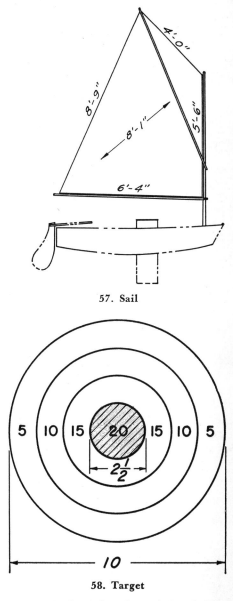

57. Sail

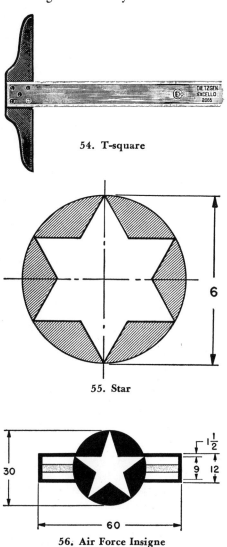

54. T-square

55. Star

56. Air Force Insigne

58. Target

5. Make a drawing of the Target shown in Drawing 58. Space the rings evenly. Draw diagonal 45° lines

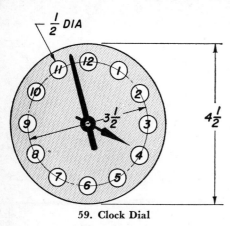

59. Clock Dial

through the bull's-eye spaced approximately $\frac{1}{16}''$ apart. Make drawing ½ size.

6. Lay out the Clock Dial Blank as shown in Drawing 59. Make full size. Omit all numbers.

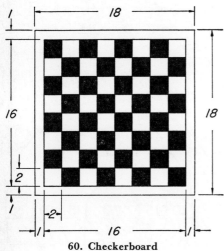

60. Checkerboard

7. Make a drawing of the Checkerboard as shown in Drawing 60. All dimensions are in inches. Select any scale.

8. By means of a drawing, determine the length of a cable reaching from a point 45' high on an antenna mast to a point on the ground 20' from the base of the mast.

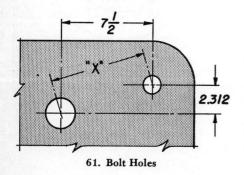

61. Bolt Holes

9. By means of a drawing, find the distance between centers of the Bolt Holes shown in Drawing 61. Check your answer by calculating the distance.

10. By means of a drawing, lay out a flat belt which runs on two pulleys spaced 7'-0'' apart. The pulleys have a 36'' diameter and a 16'' diameter.

11. Lay out the Airport Marker as shown in Drawing 62. Use any convenient scale.

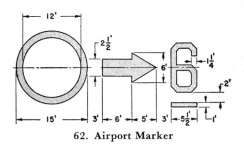

62. Airport Marker

12. Draw the Airport as shown in Drawing 63. Use a scale of $1'' = 500'$. The length of the runways are based on center line dimensions.

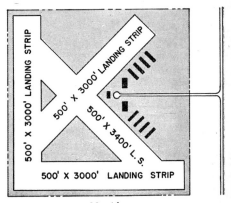

63. Airport

13. Divide your drawing paper into nine equal rectangles. See Illustration 64. Using any convenient dimensions, lay out the following construction problems:

a. Bisect a line.

b. Bisect an arc.

c. Divide a line into ten equal parts.

d. Draw an arc tangent to two lines at 90 degrees.

e. Draw an arc tangent to two lines not at 90 degrees.

f. Bisect an angle.

g. Draw an arc tangent to a straight line and an arc.

h. Draw tangent arcs.

i. Draw a straight line tangent to two arcs.

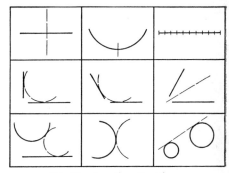

64. Construction Problems

PICTORIAL QUIZ

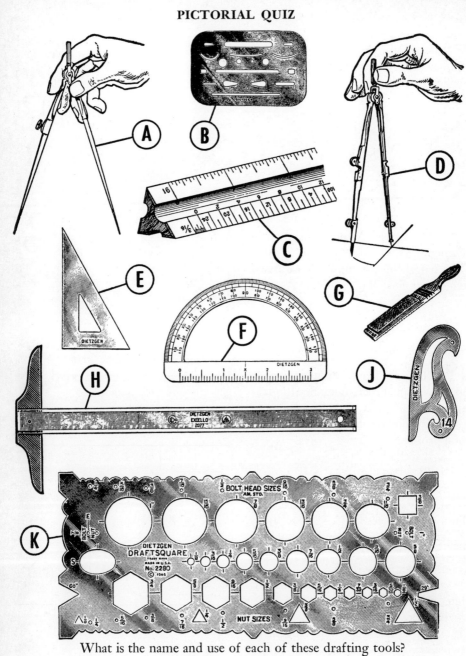

What is the name and use of each of these drafting tools?

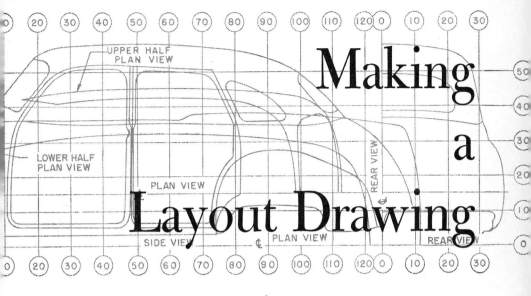

UPPER HALF
PLAN VIEW

LOWER HALF
PLAN VIEW

PLAN VIEW

REAR VIEW

SIDE VIEW   ₵   PLAN VIEW   REAR VIEW

Making a Layout Drawing

UNIT 4

From time to time, during your working or recreation hours, many of you will have to lay out an outline of some project which you wish to make. Perhaps the outline may even be for a

2. These layout men are setting up facilities for a new automotive plant.

Courtesy Ford Motor Company

1. In industry draftsmen often lay out objects full size such as these men are doing.

Courtesy General Motors Co.

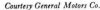

Courtesy Douglas Aircraft Co.

3. These loftsmen are preparing a layout of an aircraft section. This shows how smooth curves are drawn.

baseball diamond or a football field. Ability to make layouts is very useful.

The outline is usually drawn on paper first to get an idea of how the object will look. After the outline is completed, it is transferred onto the material from which the object is to be constructed. The process of making an outline in this manner is referred to as "layout." When first drawn on paper, the outline is known as a layout drawing. Incidentally, this type of drawing is used a great deal by architects and civil engineers. Such drawings are also used in template making and sheetmetal pattern work. In industry, the person who lays out this kind of work is called a layout man. As a matter of fact, it is common practice to lay out the full-size profile of many products before producing them. For example, in aircraft plants, the full-size shape of wings or fuselages is often laid out on the floor of huge rooms called "lofts." The process of making these full-size profiles is known as "lofting." See Photograph 3.

The purpose of this unit is to give you some specific instructions on how to make simple layout drawings.

Procedure in Making a One-View Drawing

A layout is actually a one-view drawing since it presents the shape of

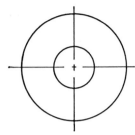

4. This washer is an example of a one-view drawing.

one surface only. It presents an object as it would be seen looking squarely at one surface, while the other surfaces could not be seen. Notice the washer shown in Drawing 4. Although this product has thickness, the thickness is not shown. The thickness is indicated by a note such as

5. This is the procedure for making a simple layout. Here you can see the order in which lines should be drawn.

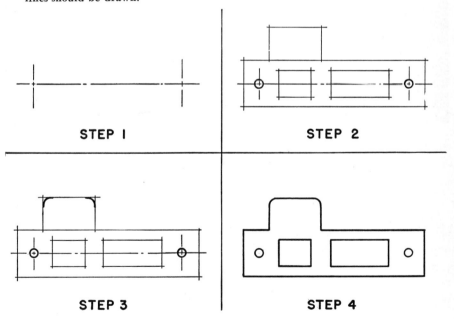

STEP 1

STEP 2

STEP 3

STEP 4

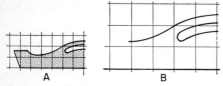

6. Laying out an object is simplified if it is drawn on cross-section paper.

$\frac{1}{16}''$ mild steel. To make a layout proceed as follows (see Layout 5):

1. Draw base lines or center lines and locate centers of arcs and circles.

2. Block in the outline of the object using light construction lines.

3. Draw circles and arcs first, then draw straight lines. Make the straight lines meet the arcs. This practice is advisable because it is easier to secure smooth connections if straight lines are drawn to the arcs than by trying to make arcs meet the straight lines.

Squared-Paper Layout Method

If an object design includes irregular curves, the layout process may be simplified by first drawing a series of squares over the object design. These squares can be drawn to represent actual measurements. The design of the object can then be transferred to the desired surface by drawing the same size squares on it. See Illustration 6A.

The design size may be enlarged (see Illustration 6B) or decreased, by proportionately enlarging or decreasing the squares.

SELF QUIZ

1. What is meant by a layout drawing?

2. For what purpose are layout drawings used?

3. What is meant by "lofting"?

4. Why is a layout drawing referred to as a one-view drawing?

5. In a layout drawing, how is the thickness of the object indicated?

6. What is the first step in making a layout drawing?

7. Why should arcs be drawn first?

8. What is the advantage of using squares in making a layout?

9. How large should the squares be?

10. If the original design is made on $\frac{1}{4}''$ squares and you want to enlarge the design five times, how large would you make the squares?

PROBLEMS

1. On A-size drawing paper construct a layout of the Football Gridiron shown in Layout 7. Choose proper scale. Omit dimensions.

2. On A-size drawing paper lay out the Softball Diamond shown in Layout 8. The size of home plate is shown in the drawing at the right. Choose appropriate scale. Omit dimensions.

3. On A-size drawing paper make a layout of the Basketball Court. See

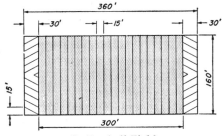

7. Football Field

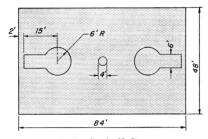

9. Basketball Court

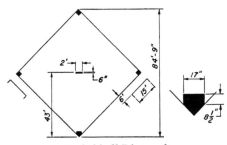

8. Softball Diamond

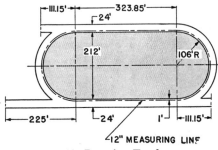

10. Running Track

Layout 9. Do not dimension. Choose as large a scale as possible for good appearance.

4. On B-size drawing paper lay out the Running Track shown in Layout 10. Use a civil engineer's scale. Let $1'' = 50'$. Approximate as closely as possible the fractional parts of a foot. Omit dimensions.

5. Enlarge the drawing of the Letter Opener in Layout 11 to full size. Use a large French curve to line up points on the outline.

6. Enlarge the pattern of the Cutting Board shown in Layout 12 on squared layout paper. Cut out the layout for the pattern.

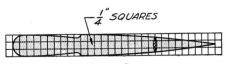

11. Letter Opener

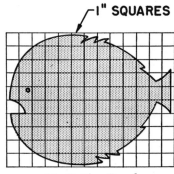

12. Cutting Board

Making a Layout Drawing **49**

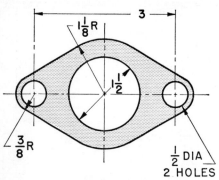

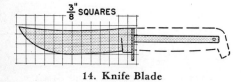

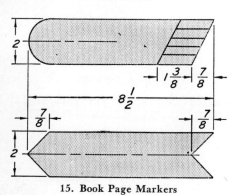

13. **Manifold Gasket**

14. **Knife Blade**

15. **Book Page Markers**

16. **Knife Sheath**

7. Construct a one-view drawing of the Manifold Gasket shown in Drawing 13. Use full scale. Omit dimensions.

8. Make a full-size pattern of the Knife Blade shown in Layout 14.

9. Make full-size layouts of the leather Book Page Markers shown in Drawing 15.

10. Make full-size patterns of the pieces needed for a Knife Sheath. See Layout 16.

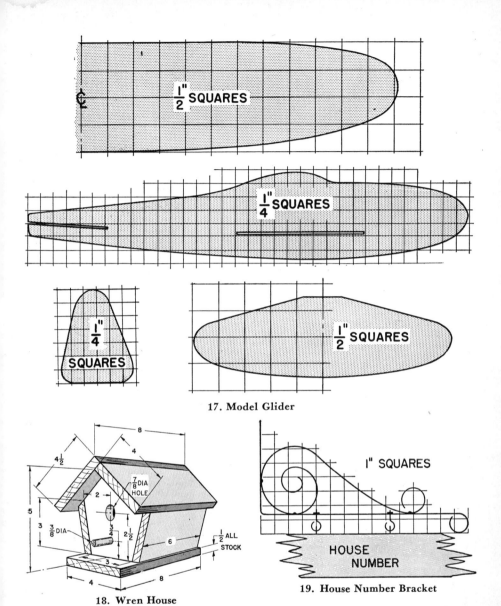

½" SQUARES

¼" SQUARES

¼" SQUARES

½" SQUARES

17. Model Glider

8
4
4½
⅞ DIA HOLE
2
5
3 ⅜ DIA
¾
2½
6
½ ALL STOCK
3
4
8

18. Wren House

I" SQUARES

HOUSE NUMBER

19. House Number Bracket

11. Make full-size patterns of the Model Glider shown in Layout 17.

12. Prepare a full-size layout of the front piece of the Wren House shown in Drawing 18.

13. Construct a layout of the wrought iron bracket for House Numbers. See Layout 19. Use one-half-size scale.

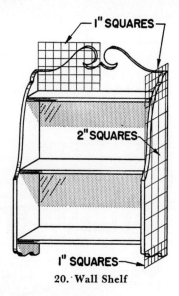

I" SQUARES

2" SQUARES

I" SQUARES

20. Wall Shelf

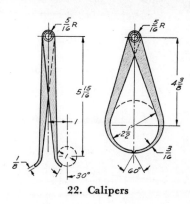

$\frac{5}{16}$ R

$5\frac{15}{16}$

$\frac{1}{8}$

30°

$\frac{5}{16}$ R

$4\frac{3}{8}$

22

$\frac{3}{16}$

60°

22. Calipers

14. Prepare full-size layouts of the scrollwork of the Wall Shelf as shown in Drawing 20.

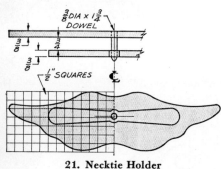

$\frac{3}{8}$ DIA x $1\frac{3}{4}$ DOWEL

$\frac{3}{8}$ $\frac{3}{4}$

$\frac{3}{8}$

$\frac{1}{2}$" SQUARES

C

21. Necktie Holder

15. Make a layout of the Necktie Holder as shown in Layout 21.

16. Lay out the Calipers shown in Drawing 22. Use full scale.

PICTORIAL QUIZ

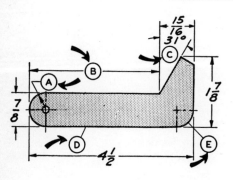

$\frac{15}{16}$

31°

C

B

A

$\frac{7}{8}$

D

$4\frac{1}{2}$

$1\frac{7}{8}$

E

1. What is the radius at A?
2. How long is B?
3. What is the angle at C?
4. In making this layout, which line should be drawn first, D or E?
5. What instrument is needed to locate the angle C?
6. What are the overall sizes of the gage?

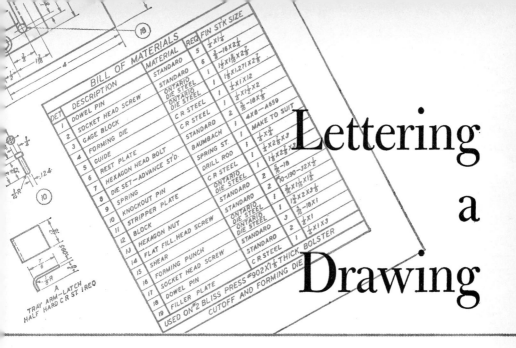

Lettering a Drawing

UNIT 5

If you examine any drawing, you will find that it contains certain printed material in the form of words and numerals. This information indicates the size of the part drawn and its relationship to other parts. It also indicates the accuracy required to make the object, the material to be used, the name of the person making the drawing and the date when the drawing was completed. The process of putting this data on a drawing is known as lettering. Since lettering is an essential part of a drawing, the letters and numerals must be easy to read. Not only should they be easy to read, but they must have a pleasing appearance. Every draftsman must learn to letter rapidly and neatly. Poor lettering can mar a good drawing.

Learning to Letter

Whenever you want to do something well, you know that practice is necessary. If, for example, you want to throw a good curve or catch a fly-ball, you have to practice throwing and catching a baseball over and over again. The more you practice, the better you become. Learning to letter also requires practice. Remember, a drawing may be excellent in all respects and yet be considered poor because of improper lettering. The material in this unit will tell you how to do good lettering.

Type of Lettering

The accepted lettering standard for most drafting purposes is known as the single-stroke *Gothic* alphabet. The let-

A B C D E F G H I
J K L M N O P Q R
S T U V W X Y Z &
1 2 3 4 5 6 7 8 9 0

1. This is the style of vertical letters used by draftsmen. The small arrows show the direction of the stroke in making the letters.

ters can be either vertical or slanted. Check Illustrations 1 and 2 and note the difference in style.

Although some draftsmen use both *upper case* (capital) and *lower case* (small) letters, the general practice today is to use all upper case letters. However, there is no specific rule as to whether the lettering should be of the slant or vertical type. Insofar as you are concerned, try out both styles and then concentrate on the one that appeals to you more and that you can make easier.

Forming Letters and Numbers

There are two things you must keep in mind to form letters and numbers correctly: (1) letters and numbers vary in width and (2) the strokes in making letters and numbers must follow a certain direction. This is true for both vertical and slant letters.

If you study Illustration 3, you will see the variation in widths of letters. The difference in width gives the letters more pleasing proportions. Thus, some letters are almost as wide as they are high, while others are slightly narrower. To give you a better idea of the relationship between width and height, the letters are reproduced in blocks consisting of six squares high and six squares wide. As a matter of fact, blocks containing any number of squares may be used depending on the size of the letters required. Keep in mind, however, that these blocks simply show the relationship of the height to the width of the letter.

Most letters are approximately two-thirds as wide as they are high. Let-

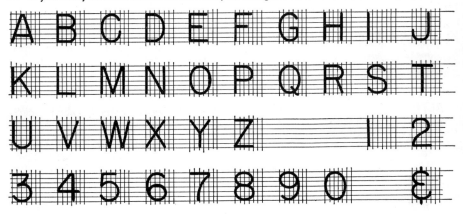

A B C D E F G H I
J K L M N O P Q R
S T U V W X Y Z &
1 2 3 4 5 6 7 8 9 0

2. Some draftsmen use the slanted letters. Guide lines may be used to help maintain a uniform slant.

ters B, C, D, E, F, G, etc., are four squares wide. Others, such as A, O, Q, R, and V, are four and one-half squares wide, whereas M is five squares wide. The widest letter of the alphabet is W, which is almost six and one-half squares wide.

Illustration 3 also shows the correct proportion for numbers. Here you will see that most numbers, such as 2, 3,

3. If you study these letters and numerals you will get an idea of their correct proportions.

A B C D E F G H I J
K L M N O P Q R S T
U V W X Y Z I 2
3 4 5 6 7 8 9 0 &

7, 8, are about two squares narrower than they are high, whereas 4, 6, 9, and 0 are more than four squares wide.

Now look at Illustration 1 or Illustration 2 again, and note how the strokes are made for each letter and number. Do not try to memorize all these strokes. When you begin doing the exercises at the end of this unit, use Illustration 1 or Illustration 2 as a guide. After you have made these letters and numbers a few times, you will find yourself automatically making the strokes correctly.

Spacing the Letters and Words

Making good-looking letters is not sufficient for proper lettering. Equally important is the spacing between the letters. To secure a pleasing appearance, the areas between each letter must appear to be equal. Due to the shapes of various letters, the appearance of equal areas cannot always be obtained by simply setting the letters a uniform distance apart. The customary practice is to judge the spacing by eye. Keep in mind that less distance

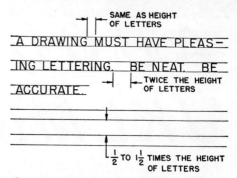

5. Notice how words and sentences should be spaced.

is required between certain letters. See Illustration 4.

The distance between words should be equal to the height of the letters. See Illustration 5. As a rule, sentences are spaced a distance equal to about twice the distance between words. When several lines are required, the spacing between them may vary from one-half to one and one-half times the height of the letters. The actual distance will depend on the amount of space that is available for the composition.

Using Guide Lines

In actual practice, the draftsman draws only two guide lines to represent the height of the letters. He then visualizes the letters to determine their correct spacing in the given area. Once he has the correct spacing, he proceeds to letter the words.

The only other guide lines that are used occasionally are slanted lines for inclined letters. These lines are drawn at random across the horizontal guide lines to help maintain the proper slant

4. Spacing between letters should be judged by eye, and not by mechanical means.

MELTING POINT

ALTHOUGH THE LETTERS ARE SPACED EVENLY, L, T, P AND O APPEAR TOO FAR APART.

MELTING POINT

MORE PLEASING EFFECT

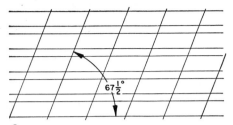

6. Guide lines are often used to help make inclined letters.

of the letters. See Illustration 6. The slanted lines should be at an angle of approximately $67\frac{1}{2}°$.

Special guide lines are usually made for fractions. Study Illustration 7 to see how this is done. Notice that these fractions are made twice as high as the whole number.

To draw guide lines, mark the height of the letters desired and with the aid of a T-square, draw two very light lines. If several lines of lettering are required, set the dividers to the correct letter height and step off the number of lines needed. With a little

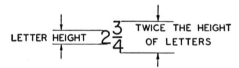

7. Each unit of the fraction should be made approximately as high as the whole number.

practice, you will soon be able to space the guide lines by eye rather than measure them with a scale or dividers.

In making slanted lines, the angle of slope must be determined. Since slanted lines are drawn at an angle of $67\frac{1}{2}°$, the proper slope may be found by marking off two units on a horizontal line and five units on a ver-

tical line. The points of termination of the two lines will produce a slant approximately $67\frac{1}{2}°$. Then using the T-square and triangle as shown in Illustration 8, draw the necessary lines.

On most working drawings, letters for notes and dimensions are made $\frac{1}{8}''$ high with $\frac{1}{8}''$ spacing between lines. Titles usually are $\frac{3}{16}''$ to $\frac{1}{4}''$ high and letters to indicate sections are commonly made $\frac{5}{16}''$ high. See Illustration 9. On large drawings, the sizes of the letters may be greater for easier reading.

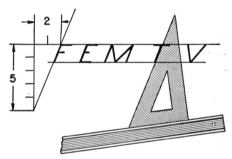

8. This is how you can find the correct slant for inclined guide lines.

Lettering Devices

Several devices are available for drawing guide lines and section lines. The two most frequently used are the Braddock-Rowe Lettering Trian-

9. This illustration shows the height of letters for various purposes.

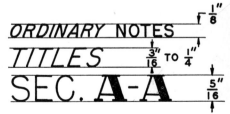

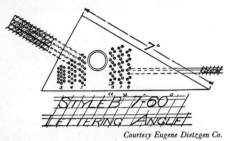

10. This Braddock-Rowe lettering triangle simplifies the task of drawing guide lines.

Courtesy Eugene Dietzgen Co.

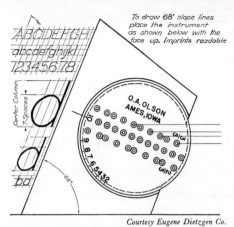

Courtesy Eugene Dietzgen Co.

11. The Ames lettering instrument is another device used for drawing guide lines and section lines.

gle and the Ames Lettering Instrument. The Braddock-Rowe Lettering Triangle has a group of countersunk holes which are used for drawing guide lines. The holes are arranged to provide guide lines for capitals and lower case letters of various heights. The numbers below each set of holes designate the height of letters in thirty-seconds of an inch. Thus, if No. 4 holes are used, the guide lines will be $\frac{4}{32}''$ or $\frac{1}{8}''$ apart. The side of the triangle is used to draw inclined guide lines. See Illustration 10.

To use this triangle, place it on the top edge of the T-square and insert the pencil point in the hole for the correct size guide line. Then slide the triangle back and forth along the edge of the T-square.

The Ames Lettering Instrument is also designed for drawing guide lines and section lines. See Illustration 11. The desired spacing of lines is secured by turning the disk to one of the numbers shown on the bottom of the disk. These numbers indicate the spacing in thirty-seconds of an inch.

Lettering with a Pencil

An H, F, or 2H pencil is used by most draftsmen for lettering. To keep the stroke of the letters uniform, rotate the pencil between the thumb and index finger after every few letters. Resharpen the pencil as soon as there is an indication that the strokes are broadening. You will find that by making your letters rapidly the strokes will be more uniform.

SELF QUIZ

1. What are the requirements of good lettering?

2. What style of lettering is most often used in mechanical drafting?

3. In lettering, why must the width of the letter be taken into consideration?

4. As a general rule, what should be the spacing between words?

5. What is the practice concern-

ing the spacing between sentences?

6. What determines the height of letters to be used on a drawing?

7. Why should guide lines be used in lettering?

8. Of what particular advantage are lettering devices?

9. What two lettering devices are most frequently used by draftsmen?

10. What kind of a pencil should be used for lettering?

PROBLEMS

1. Draw the various Traffic Signs shown in Drawing 12. Select any convenient scale. To determine the actual size of the signs, you can measure them in your area. Letter each sign using vertical letters.

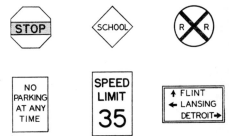

12. Traffic Signs

2. Lay out your Daily Work Schedule as shown in Form 13 on any convenient size paper. Use guide lines for all letters. Make letters ⅛″ in height. Use vertical letters for headings and inclined letters for all other information.

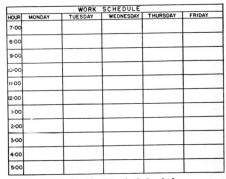

13. Daily Work Schedule

3. Draw the Baseball Score Card as shown in Form 14. Use vertical letters for headings and inclined letters for the names of the members of your team.

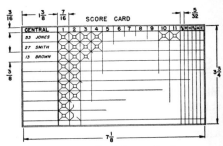

14. Baseball Score Card

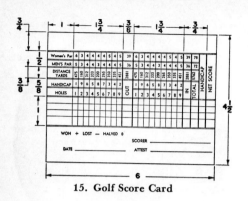

15. Golf Score Card

4. Lay out and letter the Golf Scoring Card as shown in Form 15. Use all vertical letters.

5. Letter the Problems shown in Illustration 16 and compute the answers. Also list the names of ten states and their capitals. Use either vertical or inclined letters.

$$\frac{1}{2} + \frac{3}{4} + \frac{7}{8} + \frac{3}{16} =$$

$$\frac{3}{4} \times \frac{5}{8} \times \frac{1}{2} \quad =$$

$$\frac{9}{16} \div \frac{3}{32} \quad =$$

$$\frac{3}{4} \times \frac{7}{8} \div \frac{5}{32} =$$

6. Draw the Geometric Shapes shown in Illustration 17. Letter the formulas and compute the answers for each. Use either vertical or inclined letters.

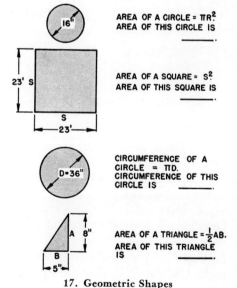

AREA OF A CIRCLE = πR^2.
AREA OF THIS CIRCLE IS _____.

AREA OF A SQUARE = S^2.
AREA OF THIS SQUARE IS _____.

CIRCUMFERENCE OF A CIRCLE = πD.
CIRCUMFERENCE OF THIS CIRCLE IS _____.

AREA OF A TRIANGLE = $\frac{1}{2}AB$.
AREA OF THIS TRIANGLE IS _____.

STATE	CAPITAL
MICHIGAN	LANSING
ILLINOIS	SPRINGFIELD
FLORIDA	
KANSAS	

16. Problems

17. Geometric Shapes

7. Measure your own Telephone Dial at home and draw it full size. See Illustration 18. Letter the numerals and letters actual size.

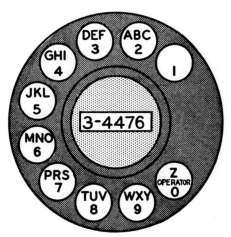

18. Telephone Dial

8. Using an outside diameter of 6″, draw the Navy Time Card shown in Illustration 19. Space circles to allow for ⅛″ vertical letters and numerals.

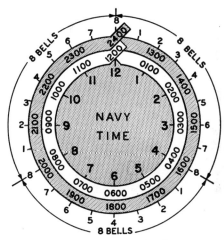

19. Navy Time Card

9. Draw the Rivets shown in Drawing 20 and letter the name of each type. Make the letters for the heading ³⁄₁₆″ high and the names ⅛″ high. Use either vertical or inclined letters.

TYPES OF RIVETS

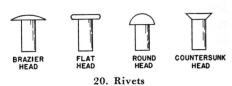

BRAZIER HEAD   FLAT HEAD   ROUND HEAD   COUNTERSUNK HEAD

20. Rivets

TYPES OF SHEETMETAL BENDS

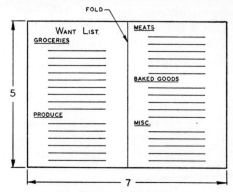

SHARP FOLD   RIGHT-ANGLE FOLD

ROUNDED FOLD   HEM

RIGHT-ANGLE FOLDS   DOUBLE HEM

21. Sheetmetal Bends

23. Shopper's Want List

10. Draw the various Sheetmetal Bends shown in Illustration 21 and letter the name of each bend. Make the letters for the heading $3/16''$ high and the names $1/8''$ high. Use either vertical or inclined letters.

12. Lay out the Shopper's Want List similar to Form 23. Then cover it with cellophane and hang it in your kitchen. If a wax pencil is used to write on it, it can easily be wiped clean and used repeatedly.

CORRECT RIVET LENGTH

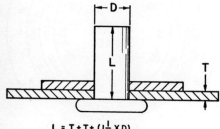

$L = T + T + (1\frac{1}{2} \times D)$
T = METAL THICKNESS
L = LENGTH OF RIVET
D = DIAMETER OF RIVET

22. Rivet Specifications

11. Draw the Rivet and Metal Pieces as shown in Drawing 22. Make the letters for the heading $3/16''$ high and the rest of the data $1/8''$ high. Use either vertical or inclined letters.

13. Design an Identification Card as shown in Form 24.

24. Identification Card

1. What is the correct name and style of letters shown in A and B?

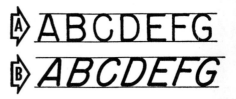

2. What is the angle of C?

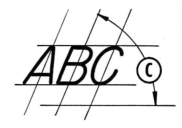

3. What should be the height of D in relation to the whole number?

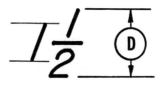

4. Does E or F have more pleasing spacing?

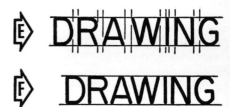

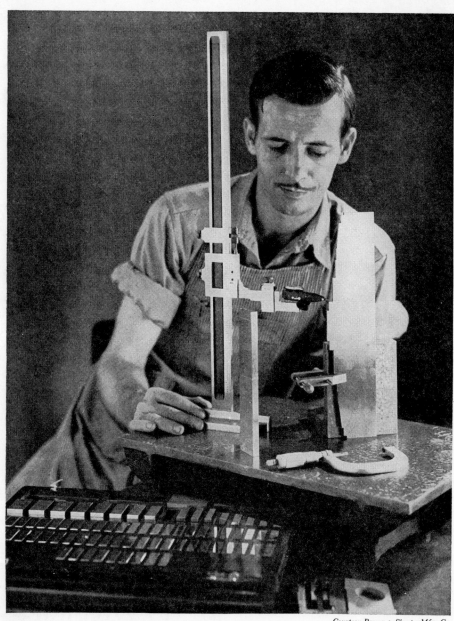

In order to read accurately the dimensions specified on a drawing, precision measuring instruments are frequently used. Here height measurements are being checked, using a vernier height gage with a dial indicator.

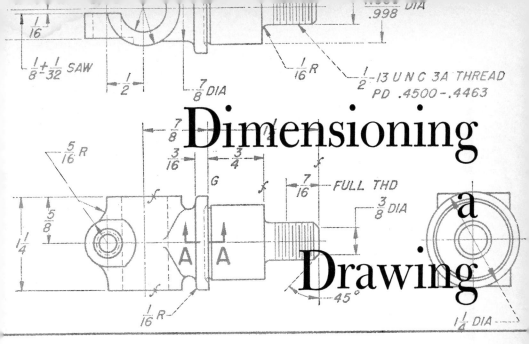

Dimensioning a Drawing

UNIT 6

If a drawing is to serve its intended function, it must not only show the shape of the object, but in addition it must contain information as to sizes of the pieces, kinds of materials to be used, the number of parts required, and such other essential data as may be needed to construct the object. The placing of this information on a drawing is known as dimensioning. In this unit you will learn about basic dimensioning practices.

How to Indicate Dimensions

The size of any part is shown by means of dimension lines with figures to indicate actual measurements. Dimension lines are drawn between extension lines which project from views. A space is left in the dimension line where the figure can be inserted, except in structural and architectural drafting where dimensions are placed above the line. Extension lines should start about 1/16″ away from the view and extend 1/8″ beyond the dimension line. See Drawing 1.

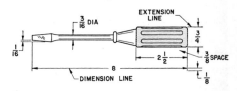

1. This is how a drawing is dimensioned.

Arrowheads, which are used on the ends of dimension lines, should be approximately three times as long as they are wide. For most drawings, they will average about 1/8″ in length. Arrowheads are drawn either with two or three strokes, as shown in Illustration 2. The important thing is to keep all arrowheads uniform in size and distinct so they are easily seen.

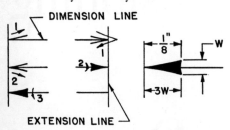

2. Notice how arrowheads are made. Two methods are illustrated.

In the past, it was the practice to place dimensional figures so as to read from the bottom and right side of the drawing as shown in Drawing 3. Al-

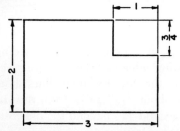

3. Some draftsmen still dimension drawings with figures to read from the bottom and the right side of the drawing.

though this system is still used to some extent today, most draftsmen now arrange all dimensions so they read from the bottom of the sheet. See Drawing 4. When dimensions are placed in a vertical position the task of dimensioning is simplified and the figures are easier to read.

When fractional dimensions are used, the dividing line or fraction bar should be in line with the dimension line, but slightly heavier in weight.

Inches are shown by the mark ″ and feet by ′ with a dash placed between feet and inches, thus 6′-8½″. See Illustration 5. On drawings that are dimensioned entirely in inches, the usual practice is to omit the inch marks.

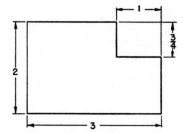

4. Most draftsmen arrange dimensions to read from the bottom.

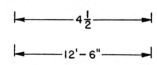

5. Inch marks may be omitted except when a drawing is dimensioned in both feet and inches.

Where to Place Dimensions

Dimensions to be of any value must be placed where they can be most easily understood. Therefore, it is important to select the view that tells the most about the object and to include the majority of the dimensions on this view. Here are a few other basic rules which are considered standard practice in dimensioning a drawing.

1. Place dimension lines between views and keep them at least ⅜″ from the view.

2. If several parallel dimension lines are used, space them about ⅜″ apart and stagger the numbers, as shown in Drawing 6.

3. Avoid repeating dimensions unless it is necessary, to understand the drawing clearly.

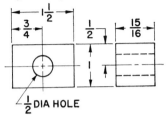

6. Sometimes it is necessary to stagger dimensions like this.

4. Locate dimension lines so they will not cross extension lines or other dimension lines. Crossing extension lines can be avoided if longer dimension lines are placed outside the shorter ones. See Drawing 7.

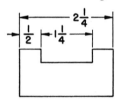

7. Keep dimension lines from crossing extension lines, if possible.

5. To reduce the possibility of confusion, keep dimensions and notes off the view. See Drawing 8. Sometimes the shape of the view is such that this cannot be done. Nevertheless, every attempt should be made to follow this practice; only as a last resort should they be located inside the view.

Dimensioning Circles, Arcs, and Angles

Centers for holes and circles are always located by means of center lines. By extending center lines beyond the

view, they can often be used in place of extension lines; however, a center line should never be used as a dimension line.

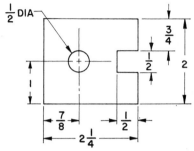

8. Always try to keep dimension lines off the view.

Always give the diameter of a circle and not its radius. On small circles, place the dimension on the outside with the letters DIA. On large circles, dimensions may be placed either on

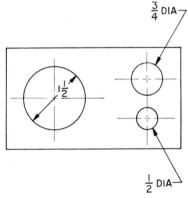

9. This is how circles should be dimensioned.

the inside or outside of the circle. See Drawing 9. Locate the dimension of holes and circles on the view where they appear as circles and not on the view where they are represented by hidden lines. See Illustration 10. When

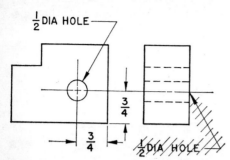

10. Do not dimension circles where they appear as hidden lines.

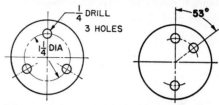

12. (Left) This is the correct way to dimension equally spaced circles.

13. (Right) One way to dimension unequally spaced holes is by indicating their angle.

dimensioning the size of holes, the leader is drawn at some convenient angle with the triangle, usually 60° or 45°, with the arrow touching the edge of the circle. See Illustration 11. Notice that if extended, the leader would go through the center of the circle.

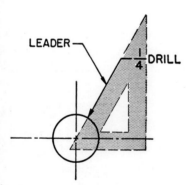

11. Notice how the leader is drawn to dimension a circle.

When equally spaced holes are located around a circle, give the diameter of the circle across the circular center line and the number and size of the holes in a note. See Drawing 12. If the holes are unequally spaced, show the angle of the holes as illustrated in Drawing 13 or by offsets as in Drawing 14, giving distances to center lines.

Arcs should always be indicated by their radius followed by the letter R. See Illustration 15.

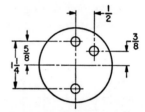

14. Another way to dimension unequally spaced holes is to offset the dimensions.

Angular dimensions are placed to read from the bottom of a drawing, except on large angles. On large angles the dimension is placed to read along the arc. See Illustration 16.

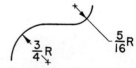

15. This is how arcs should be dimensioned.

Base-Line Dimensioning

Base-line dimensioning is a system used on certain types of drawings which deal with precision work, such as in diemaking. Dimensions on these drawings are all given from base lines

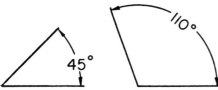

16. This is how angles should be dimensioned.

as shown in Drawing 17. This method of dimensioning reduces the possibility of errors, since each dimension is independent of the other.

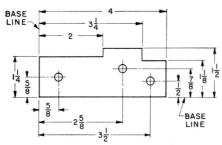

17. This is how base-line dimensioning is used on a drawing.

Notes

In dimensioning a drawing, it is frequently necessary to include information which cannot be represented by ordinary symbols of measurements. Such information is supplied by means of lettered notes. These notes are used to explain the material from which the part is to be made, the number of pieces required, type of finish, kind of fit, or any other data which the workmen may need. The important point to remember when including

notes is to make them brief, but specific. See Illustration 18.

On some drawings, it often be-

NOTES
1 - MATERIAL: SAE 1020
2 - SCALE: FULL SIZE
3 - REMOVE ALL BURRS
4 - PAINT ONE COAT GREY PRIMER IN SHOP
5 - DO NOT SCALE DRAWING

18. Sometimes it is necessary to use notes for information which cannot be shown by measuring symbols.

comes necessary to dimension a number of equal radii or holes. To repeat the radius or size of a hole several times would be a needless waste of time and would present a cluttered-up drawing. Thus, when there are four holes, for example, all alike in size and depth, only one of them is dimensioned, and a note is used to indicate that the four holes are the same. See Drawing 19.

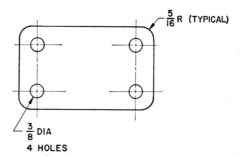

19. When a series of holes have the same dimension, use a note to indicate this fact.

In making a drawing of a casting when the internal and external edges and corners are alike in size, a note is used in this manner: "All fillets and rounds ⅛" R," or "All radii ⅛"."

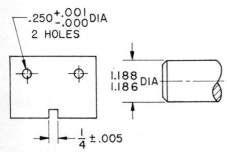

−.250 +.001/−.000 DIA
2 HOLES

1.188/1.186 DIA

¼ ±.005

20. On some drawings it is necessary to specify the tolerance that a measurement can vary.

Tolerances

For most ordinary work, drawings are dimensioned with whole or fractional numbers, such as 2, 1½, ¼, ⅛, ¹⁄₁₆, ¹⁄₃₂. When parts must be made with a great deal of accuracy, industries use a decimal system of measurement instead of common fractions. This is particularly true when pieces must be mated or are to be interchangeable. However, even with decimals, it is often impossible to produce a piece to absolute or perfect size. Accordingly, draftsmen specify an allowable error which a measurement can vary. This allowable error is referred to as "tolerance."

The amount of tolerance which is permitted depends upon the accuracy or tightness required for parts to function satisfactorily. For example, one object may have an opening of ¾", or .750". The tolerance specified may be ±.001", which means that the diameter can be .001" oversize, or .001" un-

dersize, that is, it may be .751" or .749" and be acceptable. See Drawing 20.

Finish Marks

When a drawing of a casting or forging is made, a symbol is used to indicate what surfaces are to be machined or finished. The finish mark is placed across visible or invisible lines that represent the edges of all surfaces to be finished.

Originally, the finish symbol consisted of the italic *f*. See Illustration 21. Although this symbol is still used to some extent, the practice is to designate finished surfaces by a 60-degree V as recommended by the American Standards Association. The point of the V is drawn to touch the line that represents the edge of the surface to be machined. Sometimes a code letter is inserted in the V to show the type of machining which is to be performed. See Illustration 22.

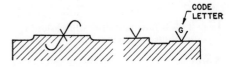

CODE LETTER
G

21. (Left) This is the old type symbol used to indicate that the part is to be finished or machined.

22. (Right) This symbol is often used to show that a surface is to be finished.

A current revision of the finish mark includes the V with a symbol to show the roughness height in microinches. In addition, a horizontal bar extends from the V on which is placed a unit to designate the waviness height. See Illustration 23.

When no surface finish roughness is to be designated, finish marks are usually omitted on holes when a note specifies the machining operation, such as "⅜″ Drill." They may also be omitted when the entire piece is to be machined, in which case a note is substituted to read—"finish all over," or "all finished surfaces to be XXX Microinches.

23. This is the current type of symbol used to show finished surfaces.

SELF QUIZ

1. What is the difference between a dimension and an extension line?

2. How large should arrowheads be made?

3. In general, dimensions should be placed to read in what direction?

4. When is the inch-mark omitted from a drawing?

5. How near a view should an extension line be drawn?

6. How far beyond the dimension line should the extension line project?

7. How far away from a view should dimension lines be placed?

8. How is it possible to prevent extension lines from crossing dimension lines?

9. Why should dimensions be kept off a view as much as possible?

10. What kind of a line should be used to locate holes?

11. When is it permissible to place a dimension within a circle?

12. How should arcs be dimensioned?

13. How should angular dimensions be placed?

14. What is meant by base-line dimensioning?

15. When are notes used on drawings?

16. What is the purpose of showing tolerances on a drawing?

17. What symbols are used to indicate the finish of an object?

PROBLEMS

1. Construct instrument drawings of the articles shown in Drawings 24 to 31. Enlarge the drawings to a convenient scale. Use any suitable size and change the design wherever you wish. Dimension all drawings completely, using the principles outlined in Unit 6.

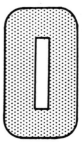

24. Escutcheon

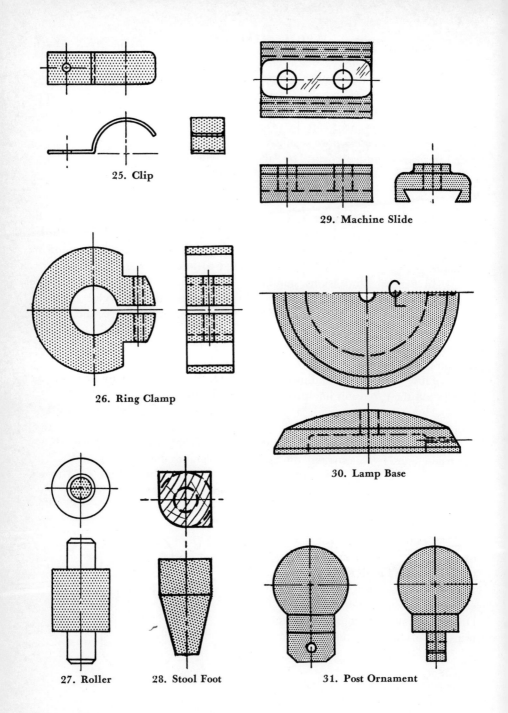

25. Clip

29. Machine Slide

26. Ring Clamp

30. Lamp Base

27. Roller   28. Stool Foot

31. Post Ornament

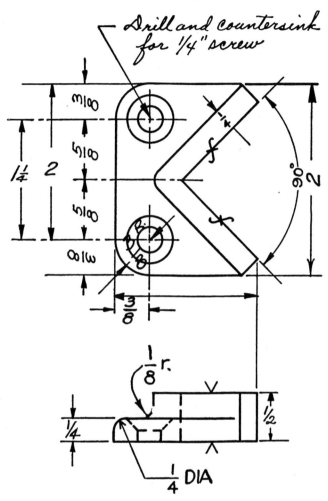

Can you pick out all the errors in this working drawing?

Courtesy The Cleveland Twist Drill Co.

From the working drawing in the background, the drill press operator has learned what operations must be done, sizes and locations, as well as the number of times the operations must be repeated on the casting.

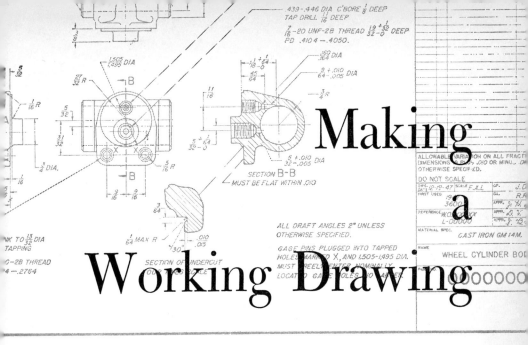

UNIT 7

The primary purpose of any drawing is to convey information. When this information is intended to show how an object is to be made, then such a drawing is referred to as a working drawing.

There are in general two types of working drawings—Detail drawings and assembly drawings. When a single part is to be manufactured, the workman usually works from what is called a detail working drawing. When a complete machine or building, for example, is to be constructed, many of these detail drawings are necessary. In addition, to illustrate to the carpenter or mechanic the manner in which the various details or parts must go together to make up the finished structure, other drawings known as assembly drawings are used. Both types of working drawings are needed to convey information to the worker on the job and make up a complete set of drawings or plans.

A working drawing must present the exact shape of the object, which means that the draftsman has to include sufficient details so the worker can easily and quickly visualize what is to be done. He does this by drawing several views of the object and by placing these views in certain positions. For relatively simple objects only two views are required, whereas for complicated objects three or more views may be necessary. In this unit you will learn how to select and locate properly the correct views for laying out a detail working drawing.

Meaning of Views

In order to get a better understanding of what is meant by the term "views," examine the box shown in Illustration 1. If you look at this box directly in front you will notice that it appears as a rectangle. The shape as is such that the bottom, rear, and both sides must also be shown to describe the object completely in one drawing.

Placement of Views

It was mentioned previously that a working drawing must not only show

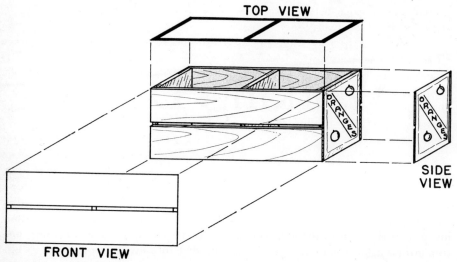

1. The principal views of an object are known as front, end, and top. Each shows the object as seen from a different position.

seen from this position is called the *front view*. Usually, since the front view alone does not present a complete picture, the box must also be viewed from the end. The shape as seen from this position is known as the *side view*.

To get a still clearer idea of the shape of the box it is necessary to look at it from another position. The third view is observed by looking down at the box from above and this view is referred to as the *top view*. As a rule, these three views are the ones most frequently used for a working drawing. Sometimes the shape of the object

various views of an object but these views must be placed in a definite relationship to each other. To understand the proper placement of views for any object, examine the pasteboard carton shown in Illustration 2. If the carton is unfolded and the sides are swung open you will find that each section falls into a definite position. Thus, the top is directly above the part that represents the front view, the sides are to the immediate right and left of the front, and the bottom is below the front. When the sides of the carton are in this flat position, all the sections are said to be in the same plane. These, then, are the positions of the various views which are included in a working drawing. The only difference is that in a working drawing the views are not shown in a connected position. Instead they are drawn with a space between them as shown in Illustration 3. Notice closely in Illustration 3 the projection of the views in their relationship to each other. For example, line *A* of the top view must always be adjacent to line *A* of the front view; line *B* of the side view must be next to line *B* of the front view, and so on.

When laying out the views, arrange them so the completed drawing is properly balanced on the paper. No specific rules can be given on how to secure a pleasing balance because the location of the views will be governed to a considerable extent by the shape of the object. The thing to remember is not to concentrate the greatest portion of the drawing near the top, the bottom, or to one side of the paper and leave too much empty space adjacent to it. It is always a good idea to lightly box in the main outline of the object. In this way you can easily adjust the views without having to do an excessive amount of erasing. See Illustration 4.

If the completed drawing is to have a pleasing appearance, sufficient space must be provided between each view so the necessary dimensions can be inserted without undue crowding. Check Drawing 5 and notice how the views are balanced and how ample the

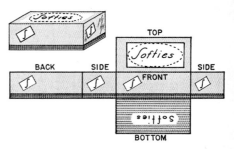

2. Notice the positions of the views when the sides of this carton are unfolded.

space between the views is for the dimensions.

Number of Views

In making a working drawing you must first of all determine the number of views that should be shown. The general rule is to include only those views that are absolutely essential to present the necessary information clearly. In other words, when one view is an exact duplication of another, then such a view should be omitted. Take, for example, the tube shown in Illustration 6. You will find that in this case only the front and side views are required. Since the top view

3. These are the correct positions of the views for a working drawing.

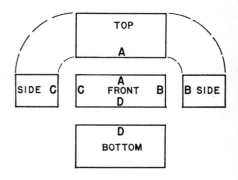

is a duplication of the front view, the top view is not needed. Notice the square box shown in Illustration 7. A working drawing of this box would need only two views—the front and top.

For many objects three views are necessary, the front, the top, and the side view. The usual practice is to show the right-side view only unless the shape of the two sides differs to such an extent that their true shapes cannot clearly be shown by a single side view. See Illustration 8. In the event the left-side view shows more of the contour of the object, then it should be used instead of the right-side view. See Illustration 9.

Occasionally, there will be some objects which will require a bottom view as well as a top view. See Illustration 10. When this problem occurs the bottom view must be included.

Projection of Views

In order to simplify the location of

4. Locate the views by boxing in their outlines like this. By planning the arrangement, you will have an idea of how the finished drawing will look.

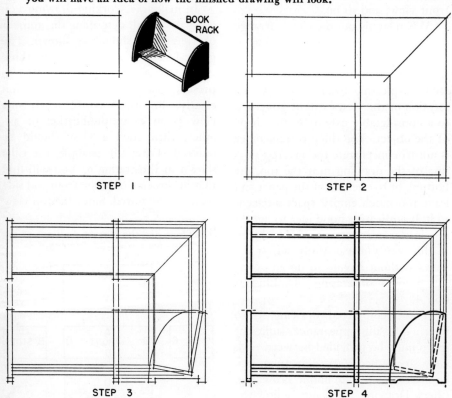

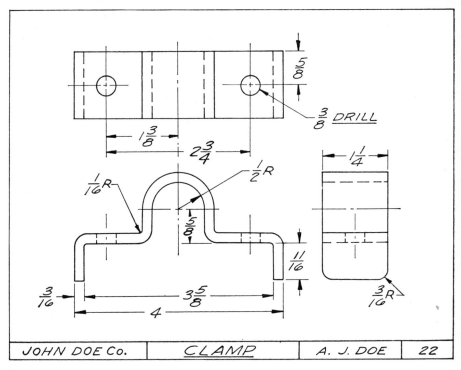

| JOHN DOE Co. | CLAMP | A. J. DOE | 22 |

5. This is how a properly balanced drawing should look. Each drawing will have slightly different arrangement, depending upon the shape of the object.

6. In this drawing only two views are required.

7. A working drawing for this box needs only two views.

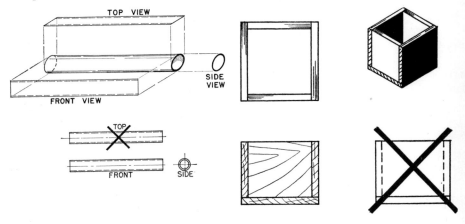

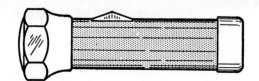

8. This object must include right- and left-side views to show clearly the correct shape of both ends.

views from one plane to another, the draftsman resorts to projection techniques, the most common of which is the one shown in Illustrations 4 and

11. The top view is located by points projected from the front view and the side view by points projected from the top and front views. Using such

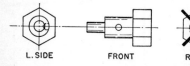

L. SIDE   FRONT   R. SIDE

9. This object is clearer if the left-side view is shown instead of the right-side view.

10. This object requires a bottom as well as a top view.

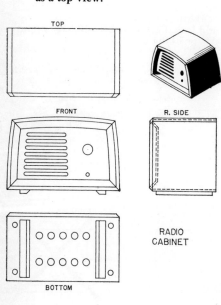

TOP

FRONT   R. SIDE

RADIO CABINET

BOTTOM

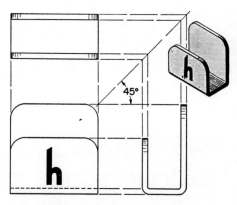

45°

11. Location of views is simplified if this projection technique is used.

12. Hidden lines are used to represent surfaces which cannot be seen.

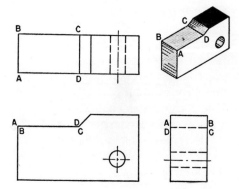

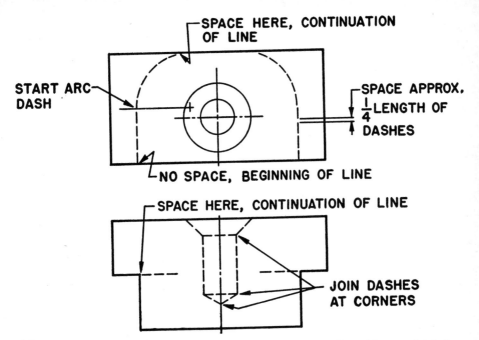

13. Study this illustration for the correct way to draw hidden lines. Observe closely how corners are indicated.

a projection method will eliminate a great deal of measuring which would otherwise have to be done.

Hidden Surfaces

In laying out the various views of a working drawing, there will be some surfaces which cannot be seen. To identify these hidden surfaces, hidden lines composed of short dashes are used. Thus, in Illustration 12 the dotted line on the side view may be considered to represent the edges *AB* and *CD* or the surface *ABCD*, and the hole is shown by hidden lines in both the top and side views.

The short dashes which form the hidden lines should be uniform in size. The practice is to make the dashes ap-

proximately ⅛″ in length with a 1/32″ space between dashes. The hidden line should always start with the dash in contact with the object line. The only exception is when the hidden line is a continuation of the full line, in which case a space is left between the full line and the first dash of the hidden line. See Illustration 13. Notice, too, in Illustration 13 that dashes for hidden arcs start and end with a dash at the points of tangency.

Curved Surfaces

When objects have curved surfaces, these surfaces may appear as curves on some views and as straight lines on others. For some objects curved lines will be seen in all views.

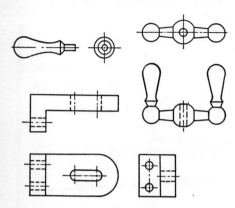

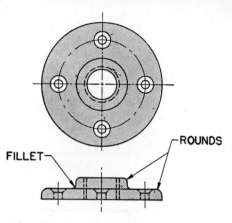

14. This illustration shows how curved surfaces appear on drawings.

15. This is how rounds and fillets are illustrated on a drawing.

Rounded Corners and Fillets

Unfinished surfaces of castings always have rounded edges where they intersect. This is done to prevent possible fracture at the point of junction.

A rounded internal corner is referred to as a "fillet" and a rounded external corner as a "round." See Drawing 15, and notice how rounds and fillets should be illustrated on a working drawing.

SELF QUIZ

1. What is the primary function of a working drawing?

2. What is meant by the term "views"?

3. What are the three principal views used in a working drawing?

4. In what position should the various views be placed?

5. What is meant by balancing the views on drawing paper?

6. What determines the amount of space that should be provided between views?

7. What determines the number of views that should be used in making a working drawing?

8. When should a left-side view be shown instead of a right-side view?

9. Why is the projection method used in locating the various views?

10. What are the important rules concerning the use of hidden lines when laying out various views of a working drawing?

11. What is the difference between a round and a fillet?

12. Why are rounds and fillets used?

PROBLEMS

1. Measure a Corner Iron as shown in Drawing 16 and draw the required views. Use full scale and include all dimensions.

2. Determine the exact size of a standard Switch Plate as shown in Drawing 17 and draw the required views. Use full scale and include all dimensions.

3. As an industrial draftsman, you might be required to draw the bicycle chain Side Link illustrated in Drawing 18. Secure exact sizes and make a one-view drawing, showing all dimensions. Enlarge drawing to a convenient scale.

4. Design a metal Strap Handle as shown in Drawing 19. Use any desirable sizes. Show the proper arrangement of views with all dimensions.

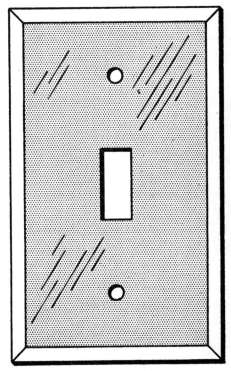

17. Switch Plate

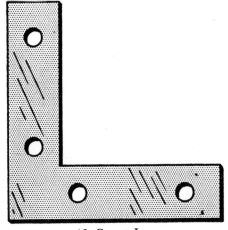

16. Corner Iron

18. Side Link of Bicycle Chain

19. Strap Handle

Making a Working Drawing 83

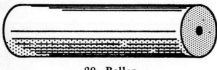

20. Roller

5. Design a roller 1½″ DIA x 8″ long with a ⅜″ DIA hole, 1¼″ deep at each end. Draw the required views and include all dimensions.

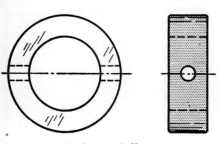

21. Spacer Collar

6. Using the illustration in Drawing 21 as a guide, construct a two-view drawing of the Spacer Collar to have an outside diameter of 2½″, and an inside diameter of 1¹¹⁄₁₆″, with a thickness of 1³⁄₁₆″. Show two holes drilled ⅜″ in diameter. Choose a convenient scale and include all dimensions.

7. Make a two-view drawing of the Spool shown in Drawing 22. Use a convenient scale and include all dimensions. Indicate that the spool is to be made of birch.

8. Construct a drawing of a Clay Plant Pot. See Drawing 23. Show all necessary views and dimensions. Place a ¼″ diameter drain hole in the center of the bottom. Select any convenient scale.

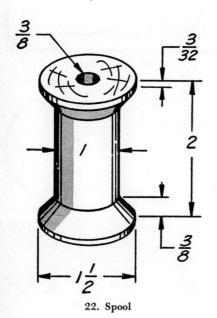

22. Spool

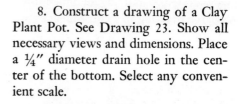

23. Plant Pot

24. Wastebasket

9. Measure a Wastebasket and produce a two-view, dimensioned drawing. Use any convenient scale. See Drawing 24.

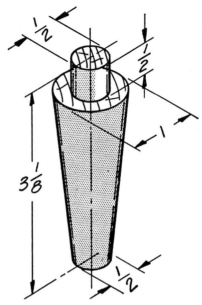

25. Doll Bed Leg

10. Drawing 25 shows a Doll Bed Leg such as you might make in your own home workshop. Choose an appropriate scale and construct a dimensioned drawing. Material—maple.

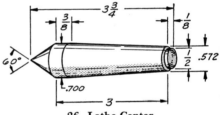

26. Lathe Center

11. Construct a two-view drawing of the Lathe Center as illustrated in Drawing 26. Material—tool steel. Show all dimensions.

12. Measure a Hitch Ball of a trailer hitch on someone's automobile. Draw the necessary views and include all dimensions. See Drawing 27.

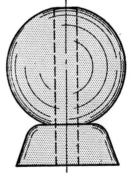

27. Hitch Ball

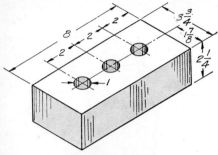

28. Face Brick

13. Construct a three-view drawing of the Face Brick showing all dimensions. Use any convenient scale. See Drawing 28.

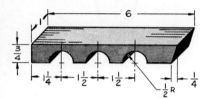

29. Footrest Adjuster

14. Using Drawing 29 as a guide, produce a dimensioned drawing of the Footrest Adjuster of a child's highchair. Material—maple. Select any convenient scale.

15. Produce a dimensioned drawing of the Hammer Head shown in Drawing 30. Material—tool steel.

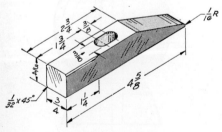

30. Hammer Head

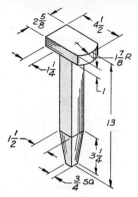

31. Stake

16. Construct a three-view drawing of the sheetmetal Stake shown in Drawing 31. Material—high carbon steel.

17. Make a working drawing of the Mallet shown in Drawing 32. Material—maple.

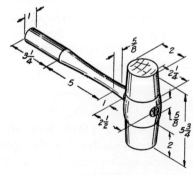

32. Mallet.

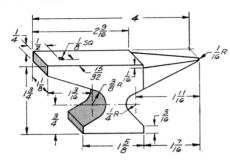

33. Anvil Paper Weight

20. Draw the necessary views of the Knife Holder shown in Drawing 35. The front piece is to be made of pine and the back of birch plywood.

18. Construct a working drawing of the Anvil Paper Weight shown in Drawing 33.

19. Make a three-view working drawing of the assembled Sleeve Board shown in Drawing 34. Omit fasteners.

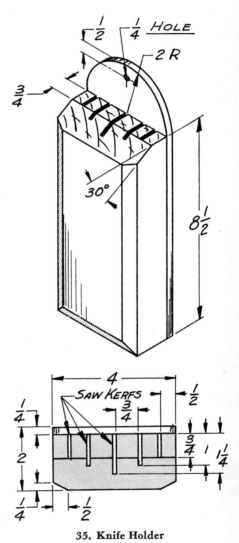

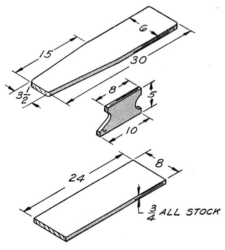

34. Sleeve Board

35. Knife Holder

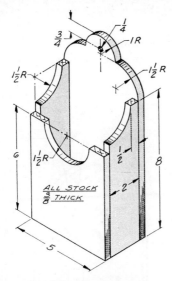

36. Colonial Letter Rack

21. Make a multiple-view drawing of the Colonial Letter Rack as shown in Drawing 36. The base is to be ⅜″ pine.

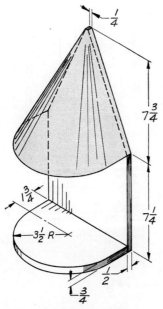

37. Potted Plant Bracket

22. Produce a multiple-view drawing of the Potted Plant Bracket shown in Drawing 37. Material—pine for bracket and sheet copper for hood.

23. Construct the necessary views of the Utility Tray shown in Drawing 38.

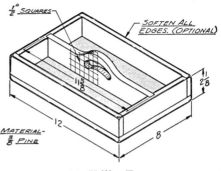

38. Utility Tray

24. Construct a two-view drawing of the Casting shown in Drawing 39.

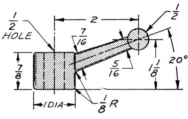

39. Adjusting Lever

25. Make a two-view drawing of the checking pin shown in Drawing 40. Use decimals for all dimensions except chamfers.

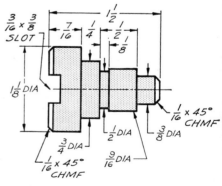

40. Checking Pin

Making a Working Drawing 89

PICTORIAL QUIZ

Match the letters of the views in the top illustration with the numbers of the views in the bottom illustration.

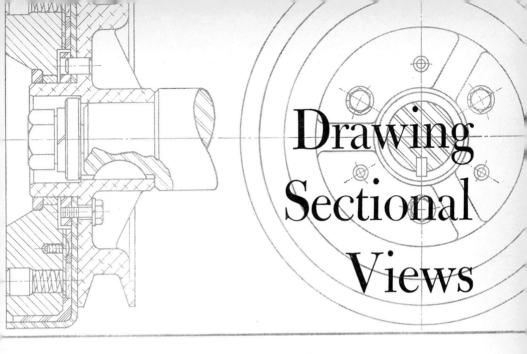

Drawing Sectional Views

UNIT 8

The internal construction of many objects is so complicated that it is impossible to show their true shape without using numerous hidden lines. The result is that the drawing is often difficult to interpret clearly. To avoid this problem the draftsman resorts to sectional views. A sectional view not only reveals the actual internal shape of an object but it also retains the outline of the external contour. The process of drawing sectional views is described in this unit.

Sectional View

A sectional view presents an object as it would appear after an imaginary cutting plane has been passed through it. The sectional view assumes that a part of the object has been removed by the imaginary cutting plane in order to show the essential interior construction details. See Illustration 1.

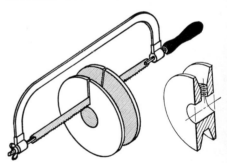

1. A sectional view assumes that part of the depicted object has been removed, so as to show the interior.

The main types of sectional views are known as full section, half-section, broken-out section, and revolved section.

The Cutting Plane

A cutting plane is shown on the principal view by means of a cutting plane line. Two types of cutting plane lines may be used. See Illustration 2.

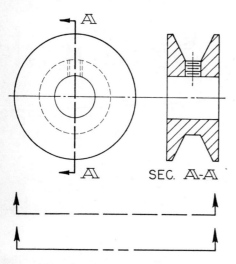

2. These are the lines used to show the location of the cutting plane.

The first type consists of alternating long dashes and pairs of short dashes. The long dashes are made ¾″ to 1½″ or more in length and the short dashes approximately ⅛″ with 1⁄16″ spaces. The second type of cutting plane line is made of equal dashes about ¼″ long. The ends of both lines are bent at 90° and terminate with arrowheads. The arrowhead should point to the direction of sight in which the object was viewed after the cut was made.

Capital letters approximately 3⁄16″ to ⅜″ high are placed behind the arrowhead. A notation is also placed under the sectional view as SECTION A-A.

On symmetrical objects, that is, when the contour on both sides is the same in size and shape, the cutting plane line is assumed to pass through the center that separates the two equal halves of the symmetrical part. On such objects the cutting plane line may be omitted. See Illustration 3.

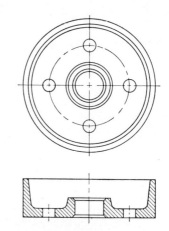

3. The cutting plane line may be omitted on symmetrical parts.

Full Section

If the cutting plane passes entirely through an object, the resulting view is considered to be a full section. See Illustration 4. The cutting plane may either pass along the main axis of the object or it may be offset.

In a working drawing the full sectional view often replaces the regular external front view. However, the top or side view may also be converted into a sectional view if the interior can be shown to a better advantage. As a rule, all hidden lines are omitted from a sectional view.

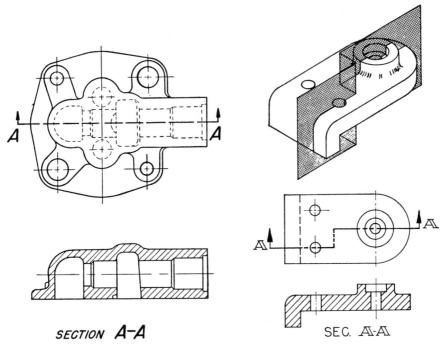

SECTION *A-A*   SEC. A-A

4. This is how a full sectional view is drawn.

Half Section

When drawing a half section, two cutting planes are passed at right angles to each other along the center lines or symmetrical axes. Passage of the cutting planes in this manner permit the removal of one-quarter of the object. See Illustration 5. A half section has the advantage of showing the interior of the object and at the same time maintaining the shape of the exterior. It is used mostly on symmetrical objects.

Broken-Out Section

On some objects only a small por-

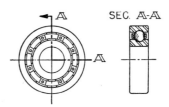

SEC. A-A

5. A half sectional view is drawn like this.

tion is necessary to show the interior construction. For such objects the cutting plane is assumed to pass through the desired feature and the interior exposed to view. The sectional area is outlined by a break line and the resulting part is known as a broken-out section. See Illustration 6.

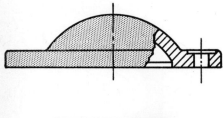

6. A broken-out section shows only a small piece removed from the object.

Revolved Section

For certain types of objects such as bars, channels, spokes or ribs the sectional view must be revolved to obtain its true shape. In this case, the cutting plane is passed perpendicularly to the axis of the object and the section is turned through a 90° angle. See Illustration 7. Frequently, the revolved section is pulled out from its position and located in some other convenient place on the drawing. This is often done to avoid cluttering up the area which contains the sectional view. A detailed section is also used when it is necessary to enlarge the removed piece for greater clarity. See Illustration 8.

Representing Sectional Views

Equally spaced lines drawn at an angle of 45° are generally utilized to represent a sectional view. See Illustration 9. There is no fixed practice that governs the spacing of these lines. As

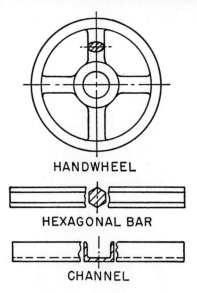

HANDWHEEL

HEXAGONAL BAR

CHANNEL

7. This is how revolved sectional views are drawn. The sectioned parts are turned through 90° in order to show their true shapes.

a rule, they should be spaced to produce a pleasing effect in keeping with the size of the object; however, they should never be closer than $\frac{1}{16}''$.

8. For some objects, the sectional view must be enlarged to show small details.

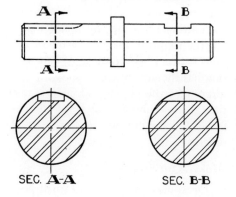

SEC. A-A   SEC. B-B

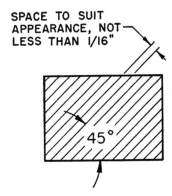

SPACE TO SUIT APPEARANCE, NOT LESS THAN 1/16"

45°

9. Most section lines are drawn at 45° angles.

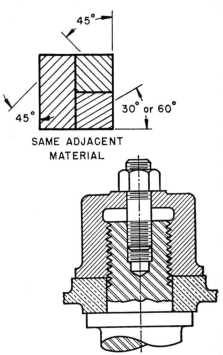

45°

45°

30° or 60°

SAME ADJACENT MATERIAL

Ordinarily, section lines should run in one direction except where there are two or more adjacent pieces. In such cases, the lines are changed to run in opposite directions so as to identify the pieces more easily. See Illustration 10. Although section lines are drawn at a 45° angle, this angle may be changed to 30° or 60° if the lines should run parallel with any part of the section outline.

The spacing should be measured by eye. The important thing is to avoid getting the lines too heavy and to preserve the unity and contrast of the sectional areas.

In sectioning very large surfaces, it is permissible to use section lines only near the outline of the sectional area with the interior portion left clear. See Illustration 11.

Symbols for Materials Used in Sections

The symbols shown in Illustration 12 are recommended by the American Standards Association to

10. By changing directions of the section lines it is easier to identify different parts.

represent various materials on sectional views. These symbols frequently eliminate time-consuming effort in preparing notes and other data needed to specify types of materials. Although these symbols do indicate the general classification of materials, they do not

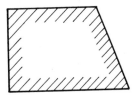

11. It is permissible on larger sectional views to section line only the outer edges of the sectional area and leave the interior part clear.

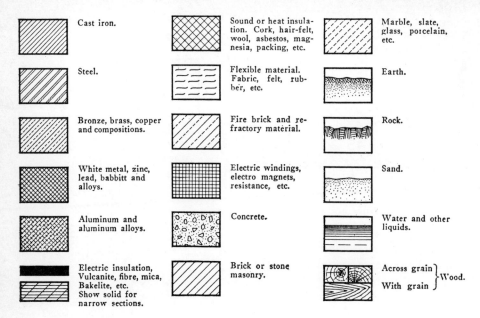

12. These symbols are often used to represent materials in sectional views.

show the exact specifications of the materials. For example, the symbol may identify the material to be steel, yet it does not necessarily state the kind of steel. When more exact specifications are necessary they are given in a note.

Sections Through Webs or Ribs

When the cutting plane passes flatwise through a web, rib, spoke, or similar objects, the part should not be sectioned. This avoids a false impression of the thickness. See Illustration 13. If, on the other hand, the cutting plane cuts across parts that are not flatwise, the section should be lined in the usual manner.

Section Through Shafts, Bolts, Pins

Whenever the cutting plane passes through the center line of such parts as shafts, bolts, nuts, rods, rivets, bearings, or other similar shapes, no section lining is needed. See Illustration 13. In instances where the cutting plane cuts across the axis of elongated parts, sectionings should be done in the regular way.

Standard Breaks

When a shaft, rod, tube or any part is too long to be shown on the drawing, a portion of the length is broken to shorten the view. The method of showing the break is shown in Illustration 14.

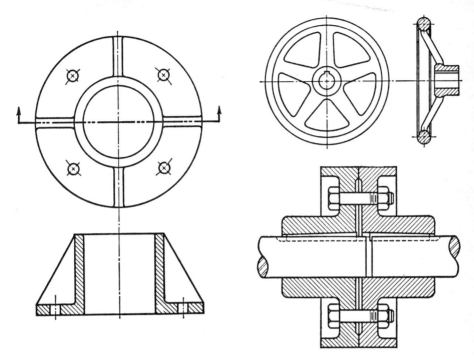

13. When a cutting line passes through a web, rib or spoke, etc., no section lines are needed on those parts.

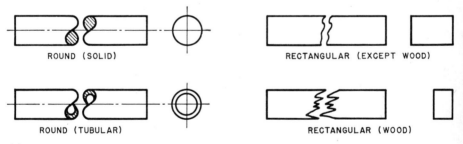

ROUND (SOLID)

RECTANGULAR (EXCEPT WOOD)

ROUND (TUBULAR)

RECTANGULAR (WOOD)

14. When an object is too long to be included on the sheet in its entirety, a portion is removed, and the break indicated with freehand break lines.

SELF QUIZ

1. When is a sectional view used?

2. What is meant by a cutting plane line? How should this line be indicated?

3. What is the purpose of the arrowheads on the cutting plane line?

4. What notation should be placed under the sectional view?

5. When may the cutting plane line be omitted on sectional views?

6. What is meant by a full sectional view?

7. From what view may a sectional view be taken?

8. What is the difference between a half- and a broken-sectional view?

9. When is a revolved sectional view used?

10. At what angle should cross-section lines be drawn on sectional views?

11. When should cross-section lines run in opposite directions?

12. What parts are ordinarily left unsectioned in sectional-view drawings?

13. Why are material symbols used in sectional-view drawings?

14. How are long objects drawn when they cannot be completely included on the sheet?

15. List some objects that would require sectional-view drawings for their manufacture.

PROBLEMS

1. Construct the two views of the Shear Pin Hub, Drawing 15, making the left side view a full section. Section-line this view using the symbols for steel shown in Illustration 12. Show all dimensions.

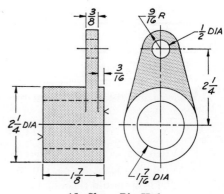

15. Shear Pin Hub

2. Construct a two-view dimensioned drawing of a standard No. 7 Grinding Wheel as shown in Drawing 16. Make the side view in full section, using the symbol for sand to represent the grit in the cross-section.

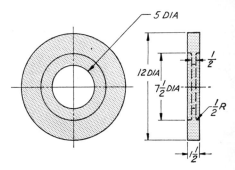

16. **Grinding Wheel**

3. Make a front and side view in full section of the Valve Handwheel shown in Drawing 17. Material is brass. Show ⅜″ diameter holes aligned in the sectional view. Place all dimensions in the proper location.

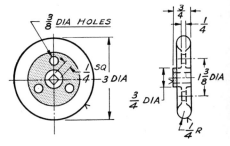

17. **Valve Handwheel**

4. Draw a two-view dimensioned drawing of the No. 11 Flaring Cup Grinding Wheel shown in Drawing 18. Make the side view a one-half section. Use the symbol slate to designate the material.

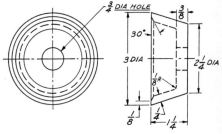

18. **No. 11 Flaring Cup Grinding Wheel**

5. Make a complete dimensioned drawing of the Truck Caster shown in Drawing 19. The side view should be in full section to represent steel. Fillets are ⅛″ R.

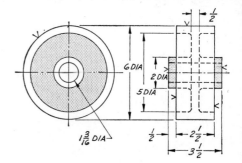

19. Truck Caster

6. Draw the proper views of the steel 6″ Std. 150 Lb. Slip-on Flange shown in Drawing 20. Make half-sectional side view. Dimension completely.

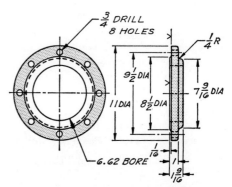

20. No. 6″ Std. 150 Lb. Slip-on Flange

7. Draw the proper views of the zinc diecast Rod Support shown in Drawing 21. Make the front view in full section.

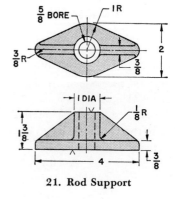

21. Rod Support

8. Make a two-view drawing of the Lever Link, Drawing 22, showing a revolved section taken at a convenient position between the hubs. Material—aluminum.

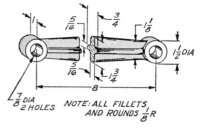

22. Lever Link

9. Construct the views of the cast steel Vise Base, Drawing 23, showing all dimensions and finished surfaces. Make a full-section front view to show the openings in the casting.

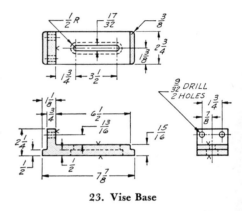

23. Vise Base

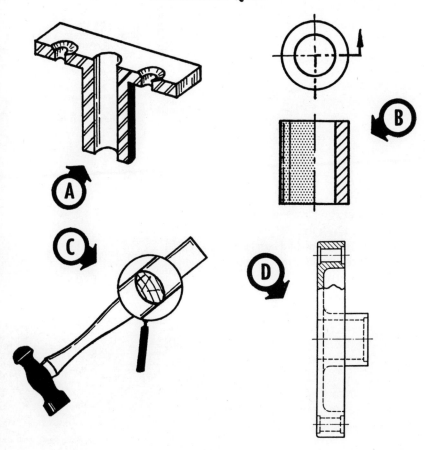

Name the types of sectional views illustrated at A, B, C, and D.

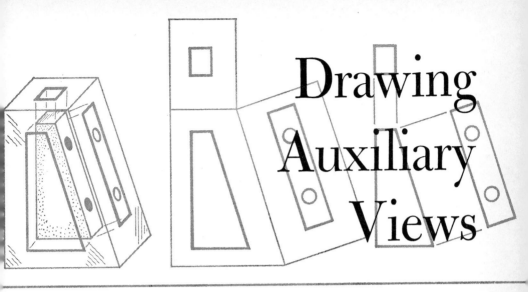

Drawing Auxiliary Views

UNIT 9

The draftsman is often confronted with the task of drawing objects having slanted surfaces which cannot be clearly shown by means of conventional views. He, therefore, has to include what are known as auxiliary views to accurately present the true shapes of these surfaces. An auxiliary view is simply a view showing the outline of a slanted surface as it appears to the observer when he looks directly at that surface.

Notice in Illustration 1 how difficult it is to get a clear picture of the slanted surface from the ordinary three views. On the other hand, if the line of sight is directly toward the slanted surface and the surface is drawn as it actually appears, then its true shape can be easily shown. The procedure for drawing auxiliary views is discussed in this unit.

Types of Auxiliary Views

Auxiliary views are classified according to the positions they assume when projected from the principal views. The first type is one in which the auxiliary view is projected from the front view. In the second type the auxiliary view is projected from the top view. The third type is one having the auxiliary view projected from the side view. From this it can be concluded that the location of the auxiliary view depends upon the position in which the object is placed when it is drawn.

As shown in Illustration 2, any auxiliary view assumes that the slanted

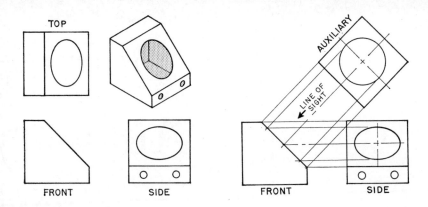

1. An auxiliary view is a view observed by looking directly at the slanted surface.

surface is hinged to one of the principal planes and when it is revolved into the plane of the paper it becomes parallel to the slanted edge.

Partial Auxiliary Views

In drawing any auxiliary view, the practice is usually to show only the inclined surface of the object and not the entire outline of the part. The use of a partial view minimizes confusing lines, improving the clarity of the view. Notice how much easier it is to read the drawing in Illustration 3 when only the true shape of the slanted surface is included as compared with the drawing shown in Illustration 4 containing the full view.

An auxiliary view will sometimes eliminate the need for one of the principal views. In such cases a complete auxiliary view will be necessary. Illustration 5 shows an object where no side view is needed since the auxiliary view fulfills the requirements of a

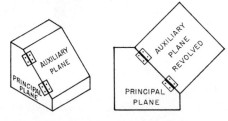

2. An auxiliary plane is assumed to be hinged to the principal plane.

3. For ease in reading, the auxiliary view should show only the slanted portion of the surface.

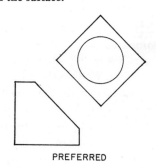

PREFERRED

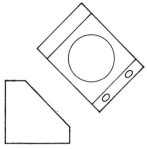

NOT RECOMMENDED

4. A full auxiliary view often complicates a drawing, as shown here.

separate side view.

When an auxiliary view is symmetrical, considerable time may be saved by drawing only half of the view. Thus in the flanged fitting shown in Illustration 6, only half of the flange is drawn since the other half simply duplicates the half shown.

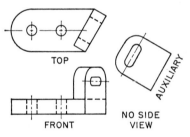

TOP

AUXILIARY

NO SIDE VIEW

FRONT

5. This auxiliary view eliminates the need for a separate side view.

Constructing an Auxiliary View from a Front View

As shown in Illustration 7, an auxiliary view projected from the front view may be positioned to the right or left or on both sides of the front view, depending on the shape of the object.

To draw this type of auxiliary view follow these steps:

1. Lay out the front and top views.

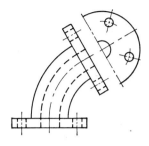

6. When an auxiliary view is symmetrical, only half of the view is needed.

2. From the slanted line on the front view, draw a reference line parallel to the edge line of the inclined surface. This reference line may be a centerline if the object is symmetrical. Locate the reference line at some convenient distance from the line of projection so the auxiliary view will not interfere with other views of the drawing. See Illustration 8.

3. From the front view, extend perpendiculars to the reference line. With compass or dividers secure the necessary depth dimensions from the top view and transfer them to the auxiliary view. Since the view is symmetrical, the centerline serves as the reference line and the dimensions are laid

7. An auxiliary view may be projected to the right or left or on both sides of the front view, depending on the shape of the object.

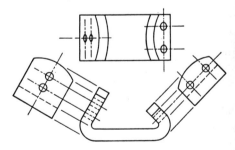

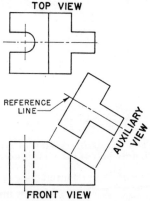

TOP VIEW

REFERENCE LINE

AUXILIARY VIEW

FRONT VIEW

8. This auxiliary view is constructed by projecting from the sloping surface of the front view.

off to the right and left of this line.

4. Complete the auxiliary view by connecting all of the transferred points.

Constructing an Auxiliary View from a Side View

1. Draw a front, or partial front, and side view as shown in Illustration 9.

2. Locate the reference line, in this case the centerline, parallel to the slanted edge found on the side view.

9. This is how an auxiliary is projected from the side view.

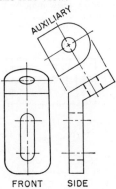

AUXILIARY

FRONT   SIDE

3. Secure the necessary depth dimensions from the front view and transfer them to the auxiliary view. Remember that the points to the right of the reference line on the front view will be on the right side of the auxiliary and those on the left will be to the left side of the auxiliary.

Constructing an Auxiliary from the Top View

1. Draw a top and front view as shown in Illustration 10.

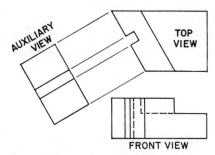

AUXILIARY VIEW

TOP VIEW

FRONT VIEW

10. This is how an auxiliary is projected from a top view.

2. Locate the reference line which in this instance may be the edge of the auxiliary view, parallel to the slanted edge in the top view.

3. Transfer the depth dimension to the auxiliary and complete the view.

Constructing Auxiliary Views of Unsymmetrical Figures

To construct an unsymmetrical auxiliary view, draw a reference line as shown in Illustration 11. Then project the necessary points to this reference line in the same manner as in working to the center of symmetrical views.

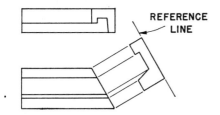

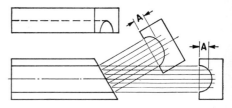

11. This is an example of an unsymmetrical auxiliary view.

12. This is how a curved auxiliary view is drawn.

Drawing an Auxiliary View Having Curved Surfaces

For an auxiliary view with a curve as shown in Illustration 12, divide the curve of the side view into any number of equal parts and project these points across to the slanted edge of the front view. From the front view project the points to the center line of the auxiliary view. Then take each distance, such as A, in the side view and lay each off on the projectors for the auxiliary view.

SELF QUIZ

1. What is the function of an auxiliary view?

2. What are the principal types of auxiliary views?

3. In drawing an auxiliary view, why is it the practice to show only the inclined surface and not the entire outline?

4. When may an auxiliary view fulfill the function of one of the principal views?

5. When may only half of the auxiliary view be drawn?

6. Describe the procedure for drawing an auxiliary view from a front view.

7. What is the purpose of a reference line?

8. How are the depth dimensions found for an auxiliary view?

9. How would you construct an auxiliary view of an unsymmetrical object?

10. How should an auxiliary view having curved surfaces be drawn?

PROBLEMS

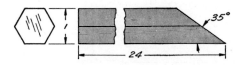

13. Pry Bar

1. Draw the end and side views of the hexagon Pry Bar shown in Drawing 13 with an auxiliary view of the slanted surface.

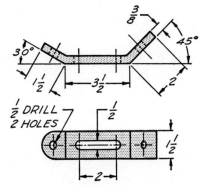

2. Draw a front, a partial top, and an auxiliary view of the two tilted ends of the Slide Adjuster shown in Drawing 14.

14. Slide Adjuster

3. Draw end, side, and auxiliary end views of the steel Spacer Block shown in Drawing 15.

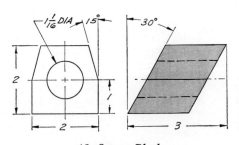

15. Spacer Block

4. Make a full-sectional view together with an auxiliary view of the tilted flange surface of the 4″ Std. 125 Lb. Elbow shown in Drawing 16. Show all dimensions.

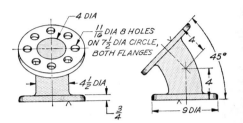

16. 4″ Std. 125 Lb. Flanged Elbow

5. Construct a front and an auxiliary end view of the oak Knee shown in Drawing 17.

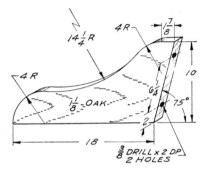

17. Knee

6. Prepare front and auxiliary views of the Slide Adjuster shown in Drawing 18. From these two views project the right side view.

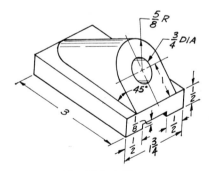

18. Slide Adjuster

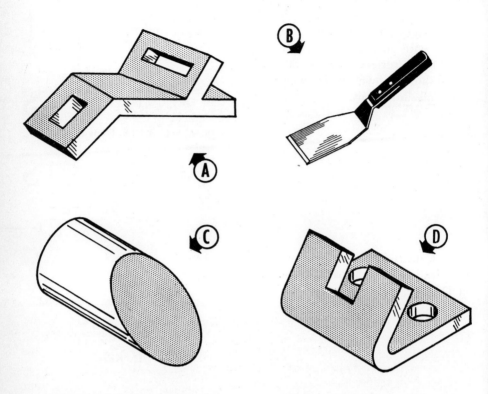

1. Name the views needed to completely show the shape of A.

2. In making a working drawing of B, why is an auxiliary view necessary?

3. What construction procedure would you follow to draw an auxiliary view of C?

4. From what principal view would you construct an auxiliary view of D?

5	1	JIG BODY—WELD	MACH. ST.	TO SUIT
4	2	SOCK. HD. SCREW	ST'D.	$\frac{1}{4}$ —20 x $\frac{1}{2}$
3	1	GAGE PLATE	KETOS TOOL ST.	$\frac{1}{4}$ x $1\frac{3}{8}$ X $1\frac{3}{8}$
2	4	SOCK. HD. SCREW	ST'D.	$\frac{3}{16}$ —18 X 1
1	2	DOWEL PIN	ST'D.	$\frac{3}{16}$ DIA. x 1
NO.	REQ.	DESCRIPTION	MAT'L.	SIZE

Learning About Assembly Drawings and Fasteners

UNIT 10

In addition to the working drawing, a draftsman is often required to make what is known as an assembly drawing. Whereas a detailed working drawing presents all the construction details of the individual parts of an object, an assembly drawing shows the object with all its pieces assembled together.

There are several types of assembly drawings, such as the unit assembly drawing, the working assembly drawing, the outline assembly drawing, and the diagram assembly drawing. In this unit each of these various types will be described as well as the different fasteners used to hold parts together, how they are shown on drawings and the methods used for specifying and noting such devices.

Unit Assembly Drawing

A unit assembly or subassembly drawing shows a number of related parts which form a group in a complicated machine or structure. Thus, in a drawing of a metal lathe, the unit assembly may consist of the various pieces of the tailstock. See Drawing 1. For an automobile, the unit assembly drawing might illustrate the assembled

1. The tailstock shown here is an example of a unit assembly drawing.

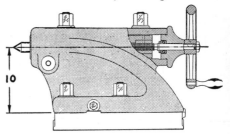

10

steering mechanism.

When sizes are included, only overall, center-to-center distances and other dimensions which may be needed to join the assembly to mating parts are shown. These are only for reference purposes, such as illustrating clearance, hole locations, etc.

Occasionally, an assembly of parts is shown in section to illustrate how the various pieces fit together. Hidden lines are usually omitted in order to avoid unnecessary confusion.

The parts may be identified by means of numbers, sometimes enclosed in systematically arranged ⅜″ diameter circles called balloons (Illustration 2). The part numbers are placed near the items they identify, with leaders terminating in arrowheads touching the individual parts. These numbers are also listed in the *parts list block* (Illustration 9), or in a *bill of materials* (Illustration 8). Sometimes the same numbers are used as references to designate the working drawings from which the individual parts have been built.

2. Here is how parts are identified in a unit assembly drawing.

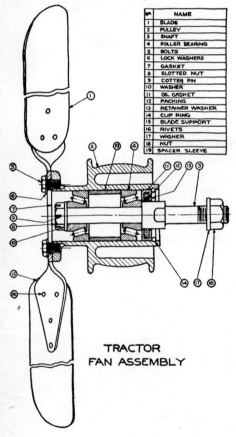

N°.	NAME
1	BLADE
2	PULLEY
3	SHAFT
4	ROLLER BEARING
5	BOLTS
6	LOCK WASHERS
7	GASKET
8	SLOTTED NUT
9	COTTER PIN
10	WASHER
11	OIL GASKET
12	PACKING
13	RETAINER WASHER
14	CLIP RING
15	BLADE SUPPORT
16	RIVETS
17	WASHER
18	NUT
19	SPACER SLEEVE

TRACTOR
FAN ASSEMBLY

Working Assembly Drawing

A working assembly drawing presents all the necessary details of a machine or structure on a single drawing. Unlike the unit assembly drawing, the working assembly drawing gives all the required dimensions, notes, and in some instances more than one view. No additional detailed working drawing accompanies this type of assembly drawing. See Drawing 3.

Outline Assembly Drawing

An outline or display assembly drawing, as it is sometimes called, is used primarily for illustrative purposes in catalogs or brochures. Frequently no dimensions whatsoever are listed except for a few overall distances. On some display drawings, a tabular dimension chart is included which specifies alternate sizes for the product illustrated. See Illustration 4 for a typical example.

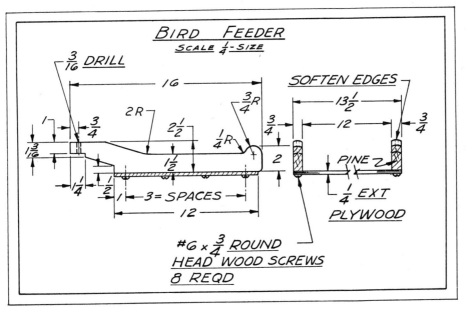

BIRD FEEDER
SCALE $\frac{1}{4}$-SIZE

$\frac{3}{16}$ DRILL — 16 — SOFTEN EDGES

2R — $\frac{3}{4}$R — 13$\frac{1}{2}$ — 12 — $\frac{3}{4}$

2$\frac{1}{2}$ — $\frac{1}{4}$R — $\frac{3}{4}$ — 2 — PINE

$\frac{3}{16}$ — 1$\frac{1}{2}$ — $\frac{1}{4}$ EXT PLYWOOD

$\frac{1}{4}$ — $\frac{1}{2}$ — 1 — 3 = SPACES — 12

#6 × $\frac{3}{4}$ ROUND HEAD WOOD SCREWS
8 REQD

3. This is an example of a detailed working assembly drawing. Notice the notes on materials, fasteners, and directions for finishing.

4. This is an example of an outline assembly drawing. Through the use of a table the dimensions for six different frames have been shown.

Courtesy U.S. Electrical Motors, Inc.

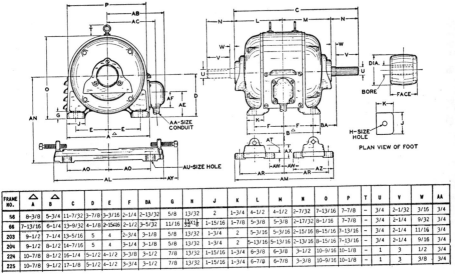

FRAME NO.	▲ A	▲ B	C	D	E	F	BA	G	H	J	K	L	M	N	O	P	T	U	V	W	AA
58	8-3/8	5-3/4	11-7/32	3-7/8	3-3/16	2-1/4	2-13/32	5/8	13/32	2	1-3/4	4-1/2	4-1/2	2-7/32	7-13/16	7-7/8	-	3/4	2-1/32	3/16	3/4
66	7-13/16	6-1/4	13-9/32	4-1/8	2-15/16	2-1/2	3-5/32	11/16	13/32	1-15/16	1-7/8	5-3/8	5-3/8	2-17/32	8-1/16	7-7/8	-	3/4	2-1/4	9/32	3/4
203	9-1/2	7-1/4	13-5/16	5	4	2-3/4	3-1/8	5/8	13/32	1-3/4	2	5-3/16	5-3/16	2-15/16	8-15/16	7-13/16	-	3/4	2-1/4	11/16	3/4
204	9-1/2	8-1/2	14-7/16	5	4	3-1/4	3-1/8	5/8	13/32	1-3/4	2	5-13/16	5-13/16	2-13/16	8-15/16	7-13/16	-	3/4	2-1/4	9/16	3/4
224	10-7/8	8-1/2	16-1/4	5-1/2	4-1/2	3-3/8	3-1/2	7/8	13/32	1-15/16	1-3/4	6-3/8	6-3/8	3-1/2	10-9/16	10-1/8	-	1	3	1/2	3/4
225	10-7/8	9-1/2	17-1/8	5-1/2	4-1/2	3-3/4	3-1/2	7/8	13/32	1-15/16	1-3/4	6-7/8	6-7/8	3-3/8	10-9/16	10-1/8	-	1	3	3/8	3/4

Learning About Assembly Drawings and Fasteners

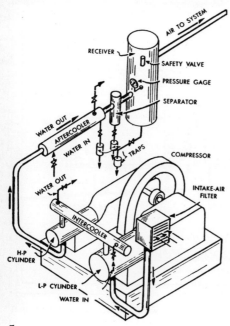

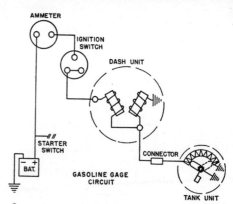

6. This is a diagram assembly drawing shown as a flat layout.

Diagram Assembly Drawing

A diagram or installation assembly drawing is used to show how equipment is erected, such as in laying out pipes or wiring. The diagram may be represented pictorially, as shown in Illustration 5, or it may be in the form of a flat layout as in Diagram 6. Oc-

5. This is a diagram assembly drawing shown in pictorial form.

7. This is an example of an exploded assembly drawing. You can see how easily a complicated mechanism could be assembled with the aid of such a drawing.

Courtesy Ford Motor Co.

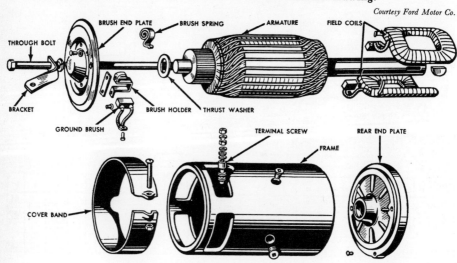

							DWG._____ B/M_____					
							NO. REQ'D_____ SHEET____OF____					
DRAWING NO.	IT. NO.	PART NO.	NO. PCS.	PART NAME		P M	MATERIAL						
							NUMBER	SPEC.	NAME	SIZE	WEIGHT	ETC.	

8. Here is a sample of a bill of material used with an assembly drawing. All essential information must be included on a drawing.

casionally, what is known as an exploded assembly drawing is used. This type shows a pictorial view of the parts in their regular order or position of assembly. See Illustration 7.

Bill of Material and Parts List

Quite often an assembly drawing contains what is known as a "Bill of Material" and "Parts List." These are usually located above the title strip or, in some cases, on a separate sheet. The bill of material includes the part numbers, the descriptive names of the parts, quantity of pieces required and kinds of material to be used. See Form 8. A parts list, on the other hand,

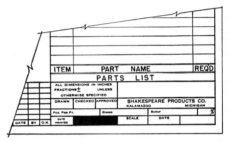

9. Here is a sample parts list for an assembly drawing.

names only the parts going into the assembly without any mention of materials. See Form 9. As a rule, when a parts list is shown, a separate bill of material is typed to go along with the set of drawings.

FASTENERS

In joining the parts of any assembly, different devices are used to fasten them together. Such devices are classified into three groups—namely, threaded fasteners, unthreaded fasteners, and welded sections. The type of fastener employed depends considerably on the nature of the structure and whether the pieces are designed to be permanently joined or to be disassem-

bled. In either case, the fasteners are always specified on an assembly drawing.

American Standard 60° V-Thread

The American Standard 60° V-thread is the most frequently used type in the United States on threaded fasteners. See Illustration 10. This 60° thread has flattened roots and crests

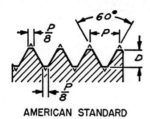

AMERICAN STANDARD

10. This is the American Standard 60° V-thread.

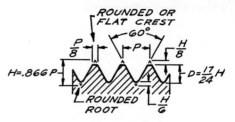

UNIFIED STANDARD

12. This is the Unified Standard Thread.

which make it much stronger than the sharp V-thread that was formerly used. See Illustration 11 for screw thread terminology. The thread is made in various degrees of coarseness which are referred to as thread series. The coarseness indicates the number of threads per inch. The common thread series are National Coarse, Na-

11. These are the common parts of a screw thread.

Courtesy Greenfield Tap and Die Co.

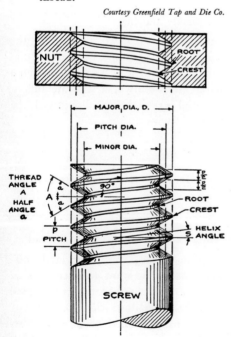

tional Fine, and National series.

Unified Standard Thread

The unified standard thread is essentially the American Standard thread. See Illustration 12. The difference is primarily in the degree of tolerance incorporated in the manufacturing process. The thread was developed as a result of an agreement signed by the United States, Canada, and Great Britain. This was done to permit greater interchange of threaded parts among these three countries.

Coarseness of Threads

The American Standard and the Unified Standard threads are made in the following degrees of coarseness:

1. *Coarse thread*, designated as NC (National Coarse) or UNC (Unified National Coarse) is a general-purpose holding type.

2. *Fine thread*, designated as NF (National Fine) or UNF (Unified National Fine) has a greater number of threads per inch and has more holding power. This thread is used a great deal in automotive and aircraft work.

3. *The 8-pitch thread series*, designated as 8N, has eight threads per inch for all diameters ranging from 1″ to

6". It is used on bolts that fasten parts which are under high pressure, such as cylinder heads or pipe flanges.

4. *The 12-pitch thread series*, designated as 12N, has twelve threads per inch for all diameters ranging from ½" to 6". It is used considerably in boiler work and on other machines requiring thin nuts on shafts.

5. *The 16-pitch thread series*, designated as 16N, has sixteen threads per inch for all diameters ranging from ¾" to 4". It is used on threaded adjusting collars and bearing retaining nuts.

Fits of Screw Threads

Threads are also made with different types of fits. The fit refers to the allowance (looseness or tightness) between the mating screw and nut. The most common fits are:

Class 1—possesses the largest allowance and is used where rapid assembly of parts is required and looseness of play is not objectionable.

Class 2—used on the bulk of standard screws, bolts, and nuts.

Class 3—used on fasteners where accuracy is very important and no looseness is permitted.

In addition to the classification number, the Unified Standard also includes the letter A or B to represent an external or internal thread. Thus, 3A represents a Class 3 fit on an external thread. Similarly, 3B indicates the same fit on an internal thread.

Tighter fits than those mentioned above require "selective assembly" and are usually experimental.

Thread Pitch

The pitch of a thread is the distance from one point on the thread to the corresponding point on the next thread. In other words, pitch is the distance between threads. A thread may be a single or multiple type. When the screw advances into the nut a distance equal to one pitch in one turn, it is known as a single thread. When the screw advances into the nut a distance equal to two pitches in one turn, it is called a double thread. A triple thread is one that advances into the nut a distance equal to three times the pitch in one turn. See Illustration 13.

A screw thread may be either right or left hand. A right-hand thread advances into the nut when turned clockwise, whereas a left-hand thread advances into the nut when turned counterclockwise. On a drawing a left-hand thread is always marked with the letters LH.

13. Examples of single and multiple threads.

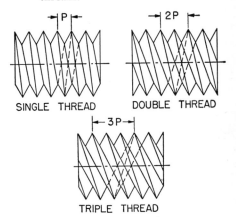

SINGLE THREAD   DOUBLE THREAD

TRIPLE THREAD

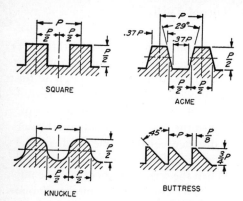

SQUARE

ACME

KNUCKLE

BUTTRESS

14. Here are a few other types of threads.

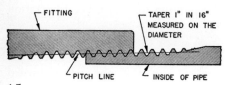

FITTING

TAPER 1" IN 16" MEASURED ON THE DIAMETER

PITCH LINE

INSIDE OF PIPE

15. This is the American standard taper pipe thread.

16. Here is how external threads are designated on a drawing.

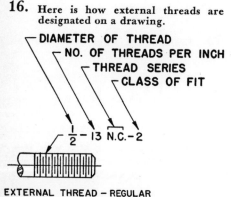

DIAMETER OF THREAD
NO. OF THREADS PER INCH
THREAD SERIES
CLASS OF FIT

$\frac{1}{2}$ - 13 N.C.- 2

EXTERNAL THREAD – REGULAR

EXTERNAL THREAD – SIMPLIFIED

Other Types of Threads (See Illustration 14)

The following are a few other threads used on threaded devices:

1. *Square Thread:* The square thread is used for power transmission but because of the difficulty in manufacturing, it has been displaced to a large extent by the Acme thread.

2. *Acme Thread:* The Acme thread is a modification of the square thread. It is a stronger thread and much easier to produce.

3. *Knuckle Thread:* The knuckle thread is one that is rolled in sheet metal or cast. It is used on such objects as electric bulbs and sockets, glass jars, and a variety of bottle tops.

4. *Buttress Thread:* The buttress thread is employed on articles where power must be transmitted in only one direction, such as on breechblocks of large guns and on jacks.

5. *Pipe Thread:* A pipe thread is used mainly on pipes which must be connected to fittings. This thread is either tapered or straight. The tapered thread is designed especially for joints that are under heavy pressure such as on fuel lines and oil fittings. See Illustration 15.

How Threads Are Designated and Drawn

Whenever a thread is shown on a drawing, four identifying features must be included. See Illustration 16. These are:

1. diameter
2. number of threads per inch

3. initial letters of the series (NC, NF, or UNC, UNF)

4. class of fit

A thread is drawn by using either the "regular" or "simplified" symbol. See Illustrations 16 and 17. To produce a regular thread symbol, crest lines representing the number of threads are uniformly spaced by eye. This spacing need not be the actual pitch distance; however, the lines should not be closer than $\frac{1}{16}$". The root lines are centered between the crest lines and terminated a short distance from the outside diameter of the thread. The simplified symbol is made by merely drawing two invisible lines representing the root of the thread parallel to the axis.

Types of Screw Threaded Fasteners

The following represent the most common types of screw threaded fasteners:

1. *Bolt:* The term bolt applies to a fastener having a head on one end and a stem that fits through a drilled opening. The opposite end of the bolt is threaded to receive a nut which can be tightened to hold parts together. See Illustration 18.

17. Here is how internal threads are shown on a drawing. Both of these methods are in common use and you should learn them.

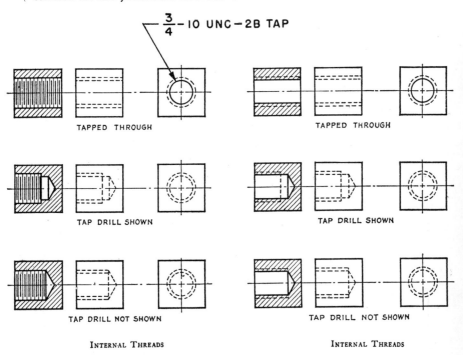

$\frac{3}{4}$ - 10 UNC - 2B TAP

TAPPED THROUGH   TAPPED THROUGH

TAP DRILL SHOWN   TAP DRILL SHOWN

TAP DRILL NOT SHOWN   TAP DRILL NOT SHOWN

INTERNAL THREADS   INTERNAL THREADS

REGULAR SYMBOLS   **SIMPLIFIED SYMBOLS**

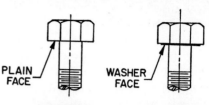

HEX HEAD   SQUARE HEAD   PLAIN FACE   WASHER FACE

UNFINISHED   SEMI-FINISHED

19. Bolt with a plain bearing surface and with a washer face.

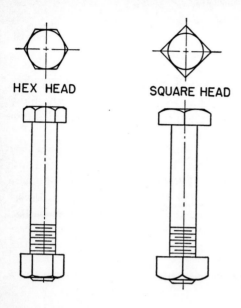

     The two main types of bolts are classified as *regular* for general purpose work, and *heavy* for use when great bearing surface is required. Bolts and nuts have either square or hexagonal heads. They are also classified as *finished*, *semi-finished*, or *unfinished*. Unfinished heads or nuts do not have machined surfaces nor are they washer-faced. Illustration 19 shows the difference between a bolt with a plain

18. These are American Standard bolts with nuts.

20. These are the steps to follow in drawing a square head bolt and nut. Notice the position of the bolt head and nut.

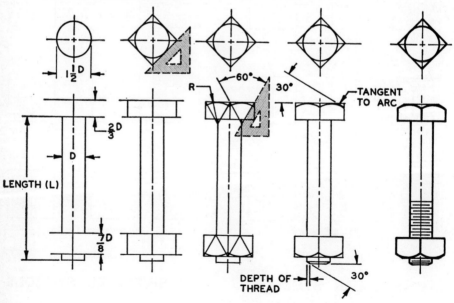

bearing surface and one with a washer face. The washer face is approximately $\frac{1}{64}''$ thick and serves as a bearing in place of a regular washer. Semi-finished bolt heads and nuts are machined or treated on the bearing surface and have washer faces. Finished bolts and nuts are the same as the semi-finished type except that all the surfaces are machined to produce a highly finished appearance.

On a drawing, the specification of bolts and nuts is included in the bill of materials. The information should show the diameter, number of threads per inch, series, class of fit, type of finish, type of head, name and length. For example, the specification would be as follows:

$\frac{3}{8}$–16NC–2 Semi-Fin. Hex. Hd. Bolt x $2\frac{1}{2}$ Lg.

or

$\frac{3}{8}$–16UNC–2A Semi-Fin. Hex. Hd. Bolt x $2\frac{1}{2}$ Lg.

To draw a bolt head and nut, secure the dimensions from the table in the Appendix and lay out as shown in Illustrations 20 and 21. A speedier method is to use a hole template described in Unit 3.

2. *Studs:* A stud or stud bolt is a rod threaded on both ends. It is used when regular bolts are not suitable, especially on parts that must be removed frequently, such as cylinder heads. One end of the stud is screwed into a threaded or tapped hole, and the other end fits into the removable piece of the structure. A nut is used on the projecting end to hold the parts together. See Illustration 22. Specifica-

21. This is how a hexagon head bolt and nut is drawn. Notice the dimensions that are expressed in terms of the bolt diameter.

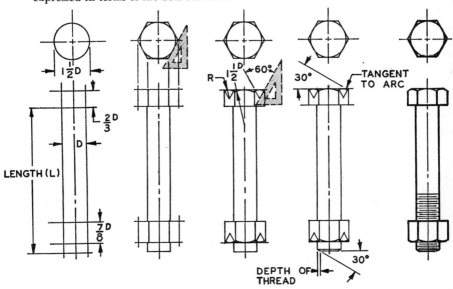

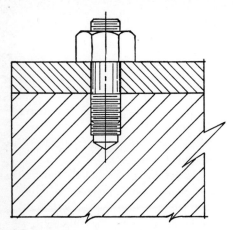

22. This illustration shows how a stud is used.

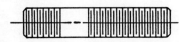

23. Here is how a stud is drawn, using the regular symbol.

tions for studs are listed in the same manner as for bolts. See Illustration 23 for how studs should be illustrated on a drawing.

3. *Set Screw:* The function of a set screw is to prevent rotary motion be-

24. This shows how a set screw is used.

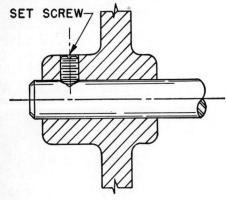

SET SCREW

tween two parts, such as the hub of a pulley and a shaft. See Illustration 24. The set screw is driven into one part so that its point bears firmly against another part. Set screws are either headless or have a square head. They are available with a variety of points as shown in Illustration 25. Specifications for set screws should include diameter, number of threads per inch, series, class of fit, type of head, type of point, and length. On a drawing this information should appear as follows:

¼–20NC–2 Sq. Hd. Oval Pt. Set Screw x ½ Lg.

or

¼–20UNC–2A Sq. Hd. Oval Pt. Set Screw x ½ Lg.

Illustration 25 shows how set screws are drawn.

4. *Cap Screw:* A cap screw passes

25. This shows various types of set screws and how they are drawn.

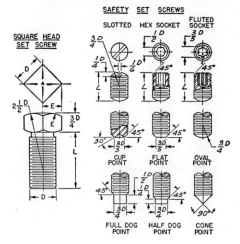

through a clearance hole in one member of the structure and screws into a threaded or tapped hole in the other. They range in diameter from ¼″ to 1¼″ and are available in five standard head types as shown in Illustration 26. Cap screws are specified in the bill of materials as follows:

½–13NC–3 Button Hd. Cap. Screw x 1 Lg.

or

½–13UNC–3A Button Hd. Cap. Screw x 1 Lg.

5. *Machine Screws:* Machine screws are similar to cap screws except that they are smaller and are used chiefly on small work having thin sections. They are specified as follows:

#10–24NC–2 Rd. Hd. Mach. Screw x ⅜ Lg.

or

#10–24UNC–2A Rd. Hd. Mach. Screw x ⅜ Lg.

Machine screws are made with four

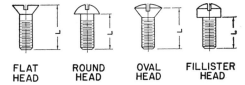

FLAT HEAD   ROUND HEAD   OVAL HEAD   FILLISTER HEAD

27. Here are some of the different types of machine screws.

standard types of heads—round, flat, oval, and fillister. See Illustration 27.

6. *Stove Bolts:* Stove bolts are used for joining parts whenever great strength is not important. See Illustration 28. These bolts are available with a round or flat head. All heads are slotted so a screw driver can be used to tighten them. Their size ranges from ⅛″ to ½″ in diameter and from ⅜″ to 6″ in length. The threads are all National Coarse. On a drawing, stove bolts are specified as follows:

$\frac{3}{16}$ Rd. Hd. Stove Bolt x 1 Lg.

7. *Carriage Bolts:* Carriage bolts are used to fasten two pieces of wood together or one section of wood to a metal member. See Illustration 29.

26. Here are examples of various types of cap screws.

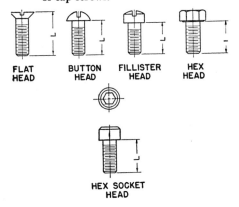

FLAT HEAD   BUTTON HEAD   FILLISTER HEAD   HEX HEAD

HEX SOCKET HEAD

28. Stove bolts like these are used when great strength is not essential.

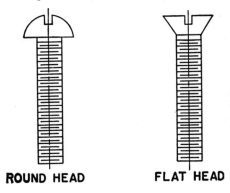

ROUND HEAD   FLAT HEAD

Learning About Assembly Drawings and Fasteners   123

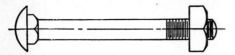

29. A carriage bolt has a square section.

This bolt has a square section directly under an oval head. The square part prevents the bolt from turning when driven into the wood while the nut is being tightened. Sizes range from $\frac{3}{16}''$ in diameter and up to 20″ in length. Carriage bolts are indicated thus:

$\frac{3}{4}$–Carriage bolt x 4 Lg.

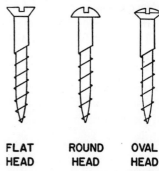

FLAT HEAD   **ROUND HEAD**   **OVAL HEAD**

30. Wood screws are made with three types of heads.

31. Self-tapping screws are available in a wide variety, for every kind of requirement.

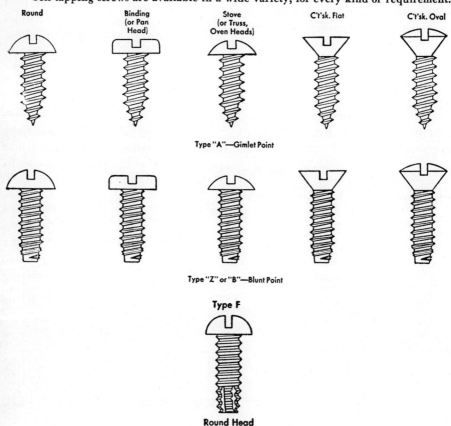

Round   Binding (or Pan Head)   Stove (or Truss, Oven Heads)   C't'sk. Flat   C't'sk. Oval

Type "A"—Gimlet Point

Type "Z" or "B"—Blunt Point

Type F

Round Head

8. *Wood Screws:* Wood screws are made of steel, brass, and bronze. Those of steel and brass are the most commonly used. Brass screws are best for fastening wooden members that are subjected to continuous dampness. Screws are available in three types of heads: flat, oval, and round. See Illustration 30. The flat head steel screws are usually sold in a "bright" finish and the round head in a "blue" finish. Sizes of screws are specified according to the length, diameter, shape of head, and finish. The following is an example of how a screw should be indicated:

1½ No. 8, F.H. Steel Wood Screw

9. *Self-Tapping Screws:* Self-tapping screws are used to fasten sheet metal parts or to join light metal, wood, plastic, or die castings. See Illustration 31. These screws form their own threads in the material as they are turned. The thread structure is somewhat similar to that of wood screws except that the steel is much harder.

Keys

Keys are used to secure parts from rotary motion such as on shafts, wheels, and cranks. Where the strain is not too severe, a round or pin key is used. For most general-purpose work, a square key is the most suitable. In addition to the round and square type, there is also available the Woodruff Key and many others. See Illustration 32. Dimensions for various keys can be found in the Appendix. On a drawing,

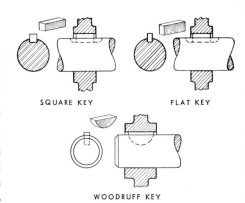

SQUARE KEY   FLAT KEY

WOODRUFF KEY

32. This is how keys are used to secure parts.

the specification for keys is shown as follows:

$3/16$ x $1¼$ Square Key
$¼$ x $3/16$ x $1¼$ Flat Key
No. 304 Woodruff Key

Rivets

Rivets are considered as permanent fastening devices and are used in joining parts constructed of sheetmetal or plate steel. They are made of many different kinds of metal, the most common are wrought iron, soft steel, copper, brass, and aluminum. Rivets are available with a flat, countersunk, button (often referred to as round or oval head), pan, and truss type of head. See Illustration 33. In specifying rivets, it is necessary to show the diameter, length, head shape, and kind of

33. Rivets are used to fasten metal parts.

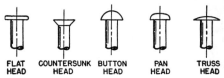

FLAT HEAD   COUNTERSUNK HEAD   BUTTON HEAD   PAN HEAD   TRUSS HEAD

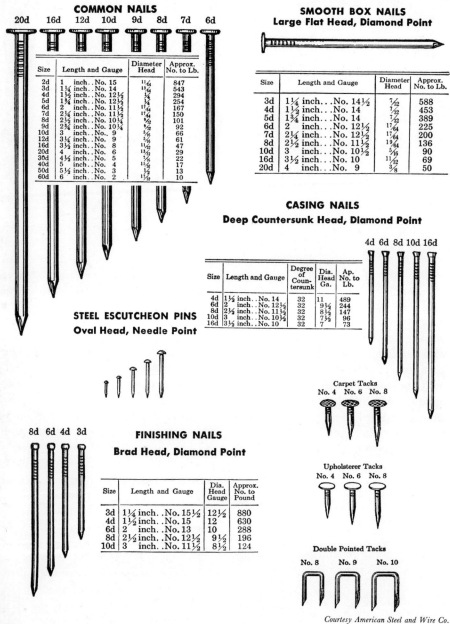

COMMON NAILS

20d 16d 12d 10d 9d 8d 7d 6d

Size	Length and Gauge	Diameter Head	Approx. No. to Lb.
2d	1 inch..No. 15	11/64	847
3d	1¼ inch..No. 14	13/64	543
4d	1½ inch..No. 12½	¼	294
5d	1¾ inch..No. 12½	¼	254
6d	2 inch..No. 11½	17/64	167
7d	2¼ inch..No. 11½	17/64	150
8d	2½ inch..No. 10¼	9/32	101
9d	2¾ inch..No. 10¼	9/32	92
10d	3 inch..No.. 9	5/16	66
12d	3¼ inch..No. 9	5/16	61
16d	3½ inch..No. 8	11/32	47
20d	4 inch..No. 6	13/32	29
30d	4½ inch..No. 5	7/16	22
40d	5 inch..No. 4	15/32	17
50d	5½ inch..No. 3	½	13
60d	6 inch..No. 2	17/32	10

SMOOTH BOX NAILS
Large Flat Head, Diamond Point

Size	Length and Gauge	Diameter Head	Approx. No. to Lb.
3d	1¼ inch...No. 14½	7/32	588
4d	1½ inch...No. 14	7/32	453
5d	1¾ inch...No. 14	7/32	389
6d	2 inch...No. 12½	17/64	225
7d	2¼ inch...No. 12½	17/64	200
8d	2½ inch...No. 11½	19/64	136
10d	3 inch...No. 10½	5/16	90
16d	3½ inch...No. 10	11/32	69
20d	4 inch...No. 9	3/8	50

CASING NAILS
Deep Countersunk Head, Diamond Point

4d 6d 8d 10d 16d

Size	Length and Gauge	Degree of Countersunk	Dia. Head Ga.	Ap. No. to Lb.
4d	1½ inch..No. 14	32	11	489
6d	2 inch..No. 12½	32	9½	244
8d	2½ inch..No. 11½	32	8½	147
10d	3 inch..No. 10½	32	7½	96
16d	3½ inch..No. 10	32	7	73

STEEL ESCUTCHEON PINS
Oval Head, Needle Point

Carpet Tacks
No. 4 No. 6 No. 8

FINISHING NAILS
Brad Head, Diamond Point

8d 6d 4d 3d

Size	Length and Gauge	Dia. Head Gauge	Approx. No. to Pound
3d	1¼ inch..No. 15½	12½	880
4d	1½ inch..No. 15	12	630
6d	2 inch..No. 13	10	288
8d	2½ inch..No. 12½	9½	196
10d	3 inch..No. 11½	8½	124

Upholsterer Tacks
No. 4 No. 6 No. 8

Double Pointed Tacks
No. 8 No. 9 No. 10

Courtesy American Steel and Wire Co.

34. Here are samples of various types of nails. You should learn to identify each kind by the correct name.

metal. For example a rivet would be designated as:

⅛D. x 1 Rd. H. Steel Rivet

Nails

There are many different kinds of nails, such as common, box, finishing, casing, and brad. Common nails have larger diameters and wider heads than other types. They are used mostly in rough carpentry. Box nails also have wide heads but are not as large in diameter as common nails. They are used extensively in box construction and in many types of carpentry where common nails would be unsuitable. Casing nails are smaller in diameter and head size than box nails. They are used especially in blind nailing of flooring and ceiling and cabinet work where large heads are undesirable. Finishing nails have the smallest diameter and the smallest heads. They are used in cabinet work and furniture construction where it is often necessary to sink the heads below the surface of the wood.

Sizes of nails are designated by the term penny (d) with a number as a prefix such as 4d, 10d. The term penny refers to the weight of the nail per thousand in quantity. A 6d nail means that the nails weigh six pounds per thousand. See Illustration 34.

Brads are the smallest type of nails. The sizes of brads are indicated by the length in inches and the diameter by the gage number of the wire. The higher the gage number, the smaller the diameter. Thus a brad would be

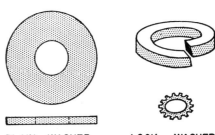

PLAIN WASHER   LOCK WASHERS

35A. These are common washers in use. designated as ¾"–No. 18.

Washers and Locking Devices

The two main types of washers are plain and lock. Plain washers are used primarily as a bearing surface. Lock washers serve as a locking device to prevent nuts from becoming loose under vibrations. See Illustrations 35A and 35B.

In addition to lock washers, other devices are often used to secure nuts.

35B. Here are some other locking devices.

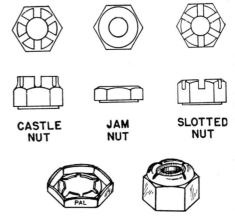

CASTLE NUT   JAM NUT   SLOTTED NUT

PALNUT   ELASTIC STOP NUT

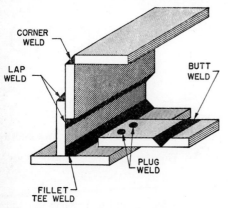

36. Types of welded joints used to join metal parts permanently.

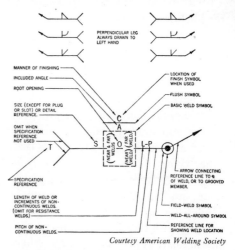

Courtesy American Welding Society

Courtesy American Welding Society

37A. This is how welded symbols are used.

The castle and slotted nuts are designed so a cotter key can be inserted in the slotted nut-and-bolt assembly. The Palnut has a slotted cone-shaped thread engaging section which when tightened is forced against the regular nut. The elastic stop nut has a red fiber locking collar that is slightly smaller than the diameter of the bolt. As the nut is screwed on, the fiber forms to the bolt thread and grips it tightly to prevent the nut from coming loose. The jam nut is simply another nut, thinner in section than a regular nut, that is screwed up tight against the regular nut.

37B. These are the basic welding symbols.

Courtesy American Welding Society

		ARC AND GAS WELDING SYMBOLS						
		TYPE OF WELD						
BEAD	FILLET	GROOVE				PLUG & SLOT	FIELD WELD	WELD ALL AROUND	FLUSH

1. THE SIDE OF THE JOINT TO WHICH THE ARROW POINTS IS THE ARROW (OR NEAR) SIDE.
2. BOTH-SIDES WELDS OF SAME TYPE ARE OF SAME SIZE UNLESS OTHERWISE SHOWN.
3. SYMBOLS APPLY BETWEEN ABRUPT CHANGES IN DIRECTION OF JOINT OR AS DIMENSIONED (EXCEPT WHERE ALL AROUND SYMBOL IS USED).
4. ALL WELDS ARE CONTINUOUS AND OF ARROW'S STANDARD PROPORTIONS, UNLESS OTHERWISE SHOWN.
5. TAIL OF ARROW USED FOR SPECIFICATION REFERENCE (TAIL MAY BE OMITTED WHEN REFERENCE NOT USED).
6. DIMENSIONS OF WELD SIZES, INCREMENT LENGTHS AND SPACINGS IN INCHES.

Welding

Welding is used considerably in fastening objects where parts are permanently joined. The basic joints for fastening welded parts are *butt*, *lap*, *tee*, and *corner*. See Illustration 36. The welding process is done with an electric arc or oxyacetylene flame.

A drawing which shows welded sections must indicate how the welds are to be made. Several years ago the American Welding Society developed a series of symbols to bring about a more universal understanding of welding practices. A few of the more common symbols are shown in Illustrations 37A and 37B.

You will note in Illustrations 37 and 39 that welding information is presented by means of a reference line with an arrowhead pointed to the welded joint. Notice the markings used to indicate the type of weld to be made. If the joint is to be welded toward the side which the arrow points, the marking is placed below the reference or arrow line. When the weld is to be made on the opposite side of the joint, the symbol is placed above the arrow line. A weld that is to be made

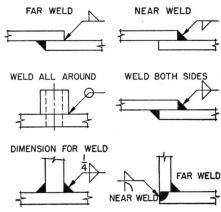

38. Location of welding is indicated by these symbols.

on both edges of the joint should show the weld symbol on both sides of the arrow line. To indicate that the weld is to be performed all around the joint, a circle is placed at the point where the arrow line is bent. A blacked-in circle means that the weld is to be done in the field rather than in the shop. The size of the fillet is shown on the left of the weld symbol and the length of the weld on the right. A tail on the end of the arrow line is used when it is necessary to insert a reference to some special information on the drawing.

SELF QUIZ

1. What is meant by a unit assembly drawing?

2. What dimensions are shown on a unit assembly drawing?

3. Why are hidden lines omitted from an assembly drawing?

4. How are parts identified on an assembly drawing?

5. What is the function of the bill of material and parts list on an assembly drawing?

6. What is a working assembly drawing?

7. What is the difference between an outline assembly drawing and a diagram assembly drawing?

8. What is the function of an exploded assembly drawing?

9. How does the American Standard thread differ from the Unified thread?

10. What type of thread is found on most commonly used bolts and machine screws?

11. What type of thread is used for transmitting power?

12. Where is the knuckle thread used?

13. When is the buttress type thread used?

14. What is meant by the lead and pitch of a thread?

15. What is the difference between an NC and an NF thread?

16. What is meant by an 8- or 12-pitch thread?

17. What is meant by the fit of a thread?

18. Threads possessing what type of a fit would you use for work that must be extremely accurate?

19. How are sizes of bolts indicated?

20. What is the difference between a finished and an unfinished type of bolt?

21. What is a stud?

22. Where is a set screw used?

23. How are sizes of set screws specified?

24. What is the difference between a cap screw and a machine screw?

25. How are sizes of cap screws and machine screws shown?

26. How are sizes of stove bolts indicated?

27. What is a carriage bolt?

28. How are wood screws specified?

29. What are self-tapping screws?

30. How are the sizes of rivets indicated on a drawing?

31. What is the function of a key?

32. What are some of the various types of keys used in machine work?

33. How are keys specified?

34. How are sizes of nails specified?

35. What is the difference between a finishing nail and a casing nail?

36. How long is a 10d common nail?

37. How are the sizes of brads indicated?

38. What means are used to prevent nuts from coming loose?

39. What type of a symbol is used to indicate a fillet weld?

40. What symbol is used to show that a weld has to be made completely around a joint?

41. What does it mean when a weld symbol is placed below the reference line?

42. How should the weld symbol be located to show that both edges of the joint are to be welded?

43. How is the size of a weld bead indicated?

44. How is the length of a weld shown?

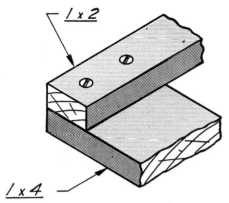

39. Wood Assembly Problem

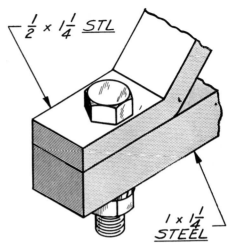

40. Assembly Problem

1. Using a woodscrew of your choice, make a two-view assembly drawing of the parts shown in Drawing 39. Specify the fastening device correctly.

2. Using a standard hex. head bolt with lockwasher and nut, assemble the parts in Drawing 40. Show two views complete with specifications for fasteners. Assume sizes not shown.

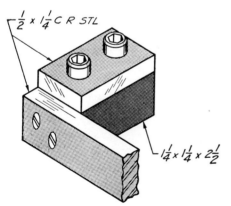

3. Using hex. socket cap screws and machine screws of your choice, make a multi-view drawing of the assembly shown in Drawing 41. Specify all fasteners properly.

41. Assembly Problem

Learning About Assembly Drawings and Fasteners   **131**

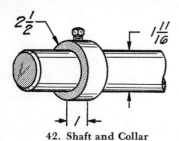

42. Shaft and Collar

4. Fasten the safety set collar to the shaft shown in Drawing 42, using a square head set screw. Diameter, length, and type of point of set screw is optional. Show two views and specify the fastener.

5. Lay out a bill of material form, and list the materials for the Folding Drawing Table shown in Drawing 43.

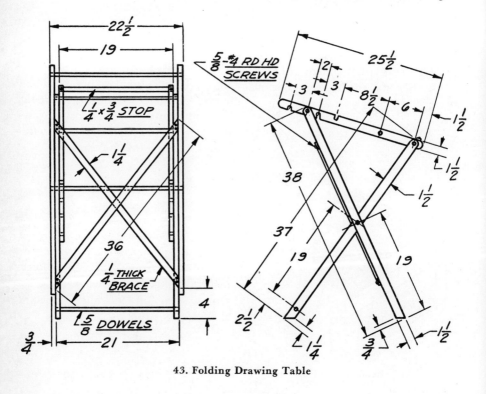

43. Folding Drawing Table

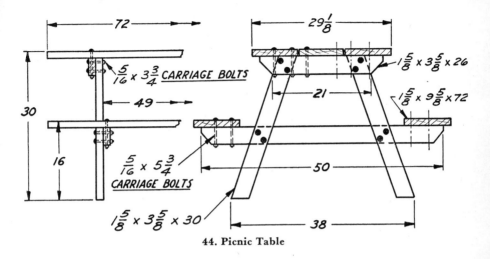

44. Picnic Table

6. Prepare a bill of materials for the Picnic Table shown in Drawing 44. Note that finished sizes are shown in the drawing. List standard commercial stock sizes for all lumber.

7. Prepare an assembly drawing of the welded Christmas Tree Stand shown in Drawing 45. Use standard symbol for the fillet weld. Design the clamping screw and show details complete with dimensions.

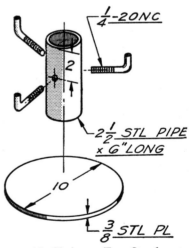

45. Christmas Tree Stand

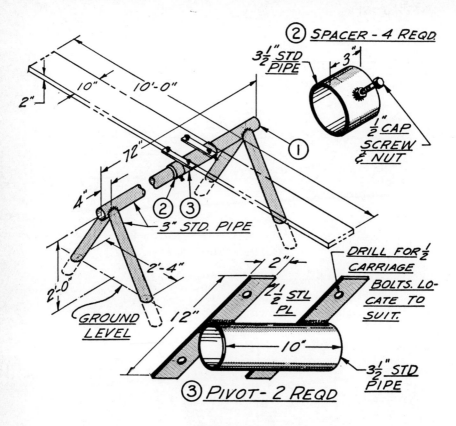

② SPACER - 4 REQD.

$3\frac{1}{2}"$ STD PIPE

3"

$\frac{1}{2}"$ CAP SCREW & NUT

①

$10"$ $10'-0"$

$2"$

$72"$

$4"$

② ③

3" STD. PIPE

$2'-4"$

$2'-0$

GROUND LEVEL

$12"$

$2"$

$2\frac{1}{2}"$ STL PL

DRILL FOR $\frac{1}{2}$ CARRIAGE BOLTS. LOCATE TO SUIT.

$10"$

$3\frac{1}{2}"$ STD PIPE

③ PIVOT- 2 REQD

46. Child's See-Saw

8. Construct welded assembly drawings of the three subassemblies of the Child's See-Saw. Show dimensions and specify fasteners and welded joints. See Drawing 46.

9. Make a one-view assembly drawing of the C-Clamp shown in Drawing 47. Include overall reference dimensions only.

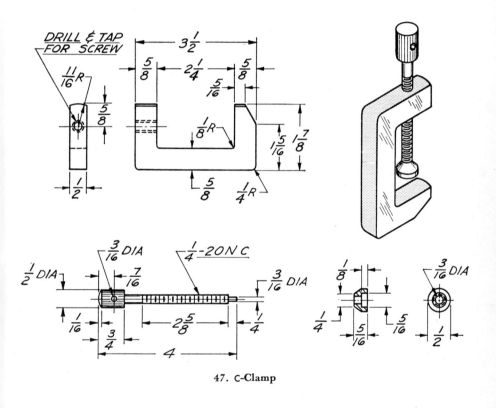

47. C-Clamp

10. Prepare a one-view assembly drawing of the Toolmaker's Clamp shown in Drawing 48. Include overall reference dimensions with clamp in closed position. Provide a parts list on the drawing.

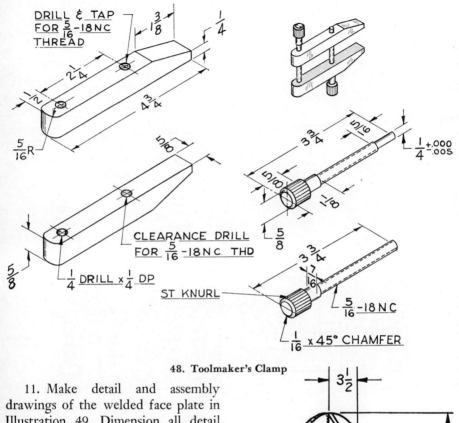

48. Toolmaker's Clamp

11. Make detail and assembly drawings of the welded face plate in Illustration 49. Dimension all detail drawings of the welded face plate in 2¾″ dia. steel bar stock. Locate 3 equally spaced holes, ⅜″ dia., on 5½″ dia. circle. Show symbols for welds.

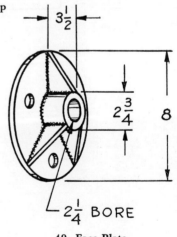

49. Face Plate

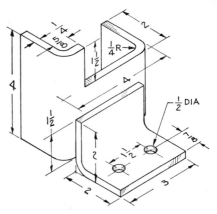

50. Weldment

12. Make a dimensional assembly drawing of the weldment, shown in Illustration 50. Use all fillet welds to join the parts. Note welds with proper symbols.

13. Construct a pictorial assembly drawing of the Playing Card Case in Drawing 51. Show the case in an open position. Select suitable scale.

14. Make an assembly drawing complete with bill of material of a project of your choice.

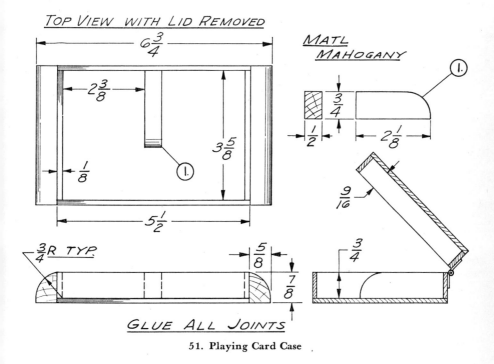

51. Playing Card Case

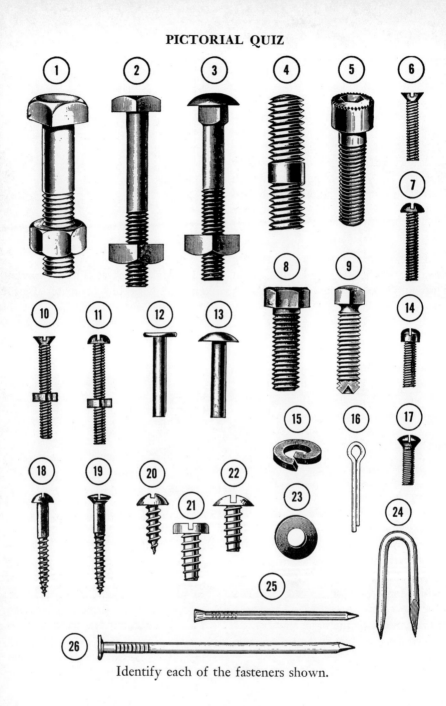

Identify each of the fasteners shown.

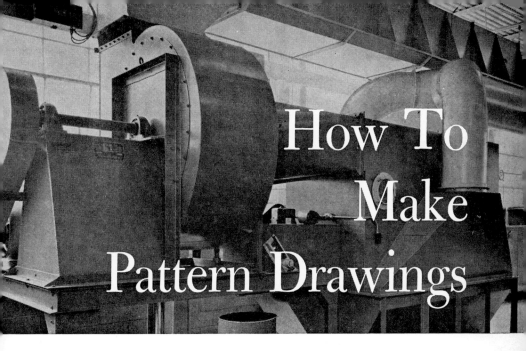

How To Make Pattern Drawings

UNIT 11

A flat layout of the surface of an object is known as a pattern or development. This form of drawing is used extensively in fabricating sheet metal products, in heating and air-conditioning work, in automotive body-work, and in the manufacture of aircraft. Patterns are also used in stone cutting as guides for shaping irregular faces, in the paper industry for laying out cartons and packages, and in the construction of numerous plastic and leather articles.

Generally speaking, the principles involved in preparing a pattern are the same regardless of the kind of material utilized. Some of the basic elements of pattern layout are discussed in this unit.

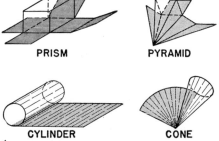

PRISM   PYRAMID

CYLINDER   CONE

1. Development refers to the unfolding of the surfaces of an object.

Developments

The development of any object consists of unfolding its surfaces so they lie in a flat plane. Most objects to be developed are shaped as a prism, pyramid, cylinder, cone, or a combination of these shapes. See Illustration 1. By means of development pro-

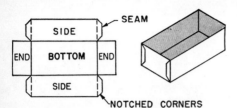

2. Here is how a square or rectangular pattern is laid out.

cedures, these shapes can be laid out accurately on a flat surface so the object can be folded to assume the correct shape.

Laying Out a Square or Rectangular Pattern

To lay out a pattern for a square or rectangular container, first draw the outline of the base as shown in Layout 2. Next draw the two ends and then the two sides. When the sections are folded along the lines of intersection you will have a rectangular box. Notice in Layout 2 that allowances are provided for seams. These seams are used to join the edges together. Observe, too, that the ends of the seams are notched. This is done to prevent too much overlapping of material where the seams join the sides of the container. The amount to provide for seams will depend on the size of the

box as well as on the method used to join the edges. Experience will teach you how best to plan the seams.

Laying Out a Cylindrical Pattern

The flat layout or stretchout of a cylinder assumes the shape of a rectangle. See Layout 3. To develop such an object it is necessary to find its circumference. This can be done by dividing the top view of the cylinder into any number of equal parts and spacing these divisions off on a stretchout line. It is also possible to find the circumference by multiplying 3.1416 by the diameter of the cylinder.

Laying Out Radial-Shaped Patterns

To lay out a pattern for a *cone*, draw a full-size front view of the cone as the triangle *ABC* in Layout 4. Using the base *BC* of the triangle as a diameter, draw a semicircle. Divide this semicircle into any number of equal parts, numbering them *1, 2, 3, 4,* etc.

With side *AB* or *AC* of the triangle *ABC* as a radius, draw an arc with *E* as a center of unlimited length to represent one boundary of the stretchout. Then draw a radius *EF* to intersect this arc at *F*. Beginning from this in-

3. Here is how a cylinder is developed.

4. This is how a radial pattern is drawn.

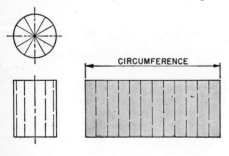

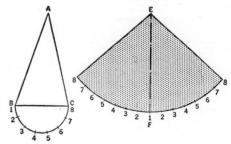

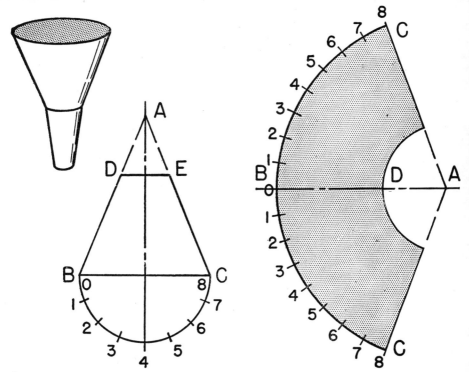

5. This is how to lay out a pattern for a frustum of a cone. The top of this cone is cut off parallel to its base.

tersection F, lay off the distances that were spaced on the semicircle through B and C. Since this semicircle represents only half of the circumference of the base of the cone, it will be necessary to lay out an equal length for the opposite half of the same arc. From the end points on the arc, draw straight lines to the center E.

Layout 5 illustrates how to draw a pattern for a *frustum* of a cone. This type of a pattern is used in laying out the parts of a funnel. The procedure is similar to the one described for a cone except that two arcs are drawn from the apex A having radii of AB and

AD. The layout shows all the details.

The method of laying out a pattern for a *truncated* cone is shown in Layout 6. Draw the front view of the cone ABC with its truncating line DE. Bisect line BC and, using BF as a radius, draw the semicircle BC. Divide the semicircle into any number of equal parts and number them *1, 2, 3, 4,* etc. Project lines from these points to the base line BC and extend them to the apex of the cone at A. Number the lines at the truncating line DE using letters K, L, M, etc.

With AB as a radius, draw the stretchout arc BB. On this stretchout line lay out the same divisions as those that were spaced on the semicircle and number them in the same order. Connect each point with the apex *A* by means of light construction lines.

Draw horizontal lines from each point on line *DE* to intersect line *AC*. Set the compass to the distance *AK'* on the front view and lay this distance on the stretchout lines *A1*. Reset the compass on line *AL'* on the front view and transfer this distance to line *A2* on

tion. Using *AB* as a diameter, draw a semicircle at the base of the cylinder. Divide this semicircle into any number of equal parts, and number the division points *1, 2, 3, 4*, etc. From these points project vertical lines to the slanting line *CD*.

Draw line *A'B'* for the stretchout, and on it space out the numbered divisions of the semicircle. From these points draw vertical lines of unlimited lengths. Project the points from the slanting line *CD* to intersect the corresponding vertical lines on the stretch-

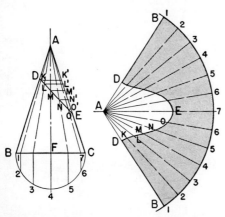

6. How a pattern is developed for a truncated cone.

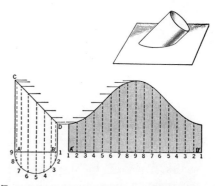

7. Laying out a pattern for the intersection of a cylinder with a flat plate.

the stretchout. Repeat the same procedure for the remaining lines and connect the points with a curved line, using an irregular curve.

Intersection of a Cylinder with a Flat Plane

Draw a side view of the cylinder as shown in Layout 7. The line *AB* represents the diameter of the cylinder, and the mitered line *CD* has the desired angle for the plane of intersec-

out. The horizontal line for point *1* on the mitered line should meet the vertical line for point *1* on the stretchout; the two lines for point *2* should meet; and so on. Connect these intersecting points with an irregular curve.

90° Intersection of Cylinders with Like Diameters

Draw a side view of two cylinders, as shown in Layout 8, one at right angles to the other. Lines *AB* and *CD* represent the diameters of the desired cylinders *H* and *K*.

On one end of each cylinder draw a semicircle and divide it into any number of equal parts, numbering the division points *1, 2, 3, 4,* etc. Draw the lines *EF* and *FG* at a 45° angle, the intersection *F* lying on the center line of cylinder *K*. Project lines through the numbered division points on both cylinders.

Draw line *A'B'* for the stretchout, and on it lay off the divisions spaced on the semicircle of cylinder *H*. Draw vertical lines through these points.

From the points where the vertical lines of cylinder *H* intersect the horizontal lines of cylinder *K*, project horizontal lines to intersect the vertical stretchout lines. Finally connect the intersections on the stretchout thus located with an irregular curve.

Draw the outline of the stretchout for the cylinder *K* by laying out the true length of the circumference of

8. This is how to lay out a pattern for a 90° intersection of cylinders with like diameters.

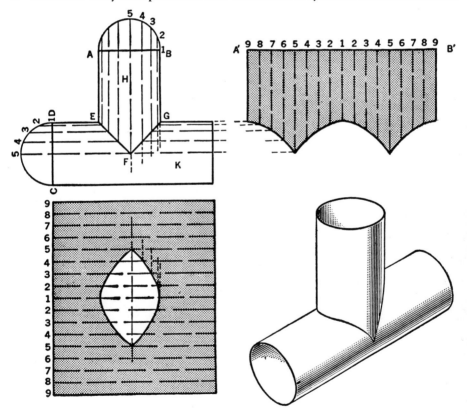

How To Make Pattern Drawings 143

that cylinder and locate the divisions as above. Then draw horizontal lines through these division points. Project vertical lines from the semicircle of cylinder *H* until they intersect the corresponding horizontal stretchout lines of cylinder *K*. Connect the intersection points with an irregular curve.

90° Intersection of Cylinders with Unlike Diameters

Draw a side view of two cylinders of the desired diameters. On lines *AB* and *CD*, Layout 9, scribe semicircles and divide each into any number of equal parts. Number the division points on the semicircle for cylinder *H*, starting at the end and running to the center, repeating the same numbers for the opposite half. Since the cylinders have unlike diameters, also draw an end view of the intersecting cylinders. Turn this view of the cylinders around to bring the point numbered *1* on the semicircle to show in the center position.

Draw line *A'B'* for the stretchout and lay out the divisions, numbering them as shown in Layout 9. The true outline of the intersection is then found by projecting lines from the end view of the cylinder *H* to the cor-

9. This is the method for laying out a pattern for a 90° intersection of cylinders with unlike diameters.

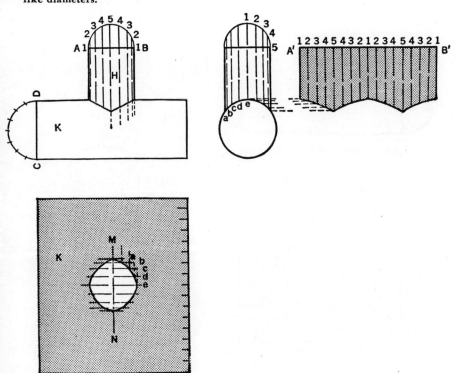

responding vertical lines on the stretch-out.

Determine the shape for the opening of the cylinder *K* by laying out the true length of the circumference of that cylinder. Draw a vertical line *MN* through the center of this layout. Starting from the point where this line crosses the middle point of the pattern *K*, mark off the distances from *e* to *d*, *d* to *c*, *c* to *b*, and *b* to *a*, these distances to be taken along the arc of the end view of cylinder *K*. Draw horizontal lines through these points. From the divisional points of the side view

of cylinder *H*, project vertical lines until they intersect the corresponding horizontal lines in the stretchout. Connect the intersection points with an irregular curve.

Angle Intersection of Cylinders of Like Diameters

The method for laying out an angle intersection of two cylinders, as shown in Layout 10, is similar to that for laying out an intersection of cylinders of unlike diameters. Any desired angle may be used. Details for making the stretchouts for the two cylinders are

10. This is the method for laying out a pattern for angle intersection of cylinders of like diameters.

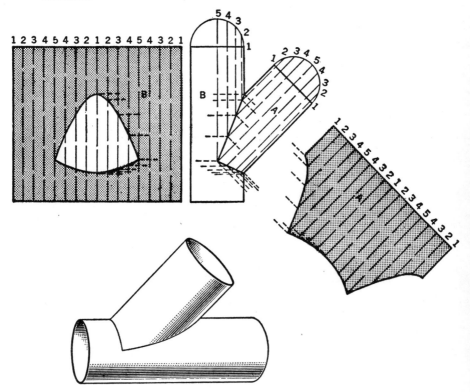

shown in Layout 10. The only point that needs to be observed is to see that the center line of cylinder *A* intersects the center line of cylinder *B*.

Angle Intersection of Cylinders of Unlike Diameters

Little explanation is required for this problem, as the procedure is prac-

11. Laying out a pattern for angle intersection of cylinders of unlike diameters is done in this way.

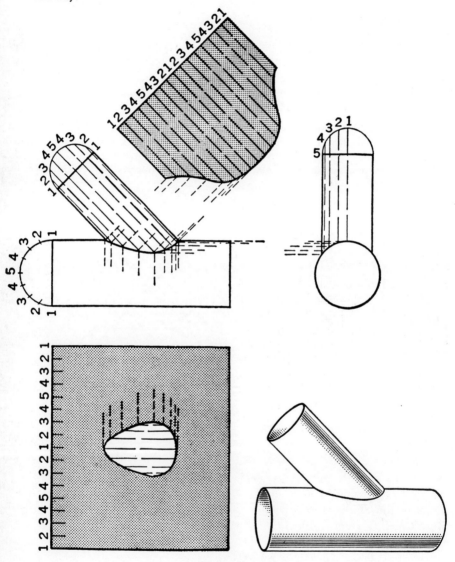

tically the same as that used for laying out the 90° intersection of cylinders of unlike diameters. To find the true shape of the angular intersection, end views of both cylinders must be drawn. See Layout 11.

Square and Rectangular Intersection

To develop the intersection of a square duct to a plane flange, proceed as follows:

Draw the front view of the square duct and the line representing the slope of the flange. See Layout 12.

Draw the top view of the square above the front view, and label the corners *1*, *2*, *3*, and *4*. Draw a horizontal line to represent the stretchout of the square. On this line lay out the distances corresponding to the four sides of the square. Start from the seam at *0* in the top view, and space off the distances *0–1*, *1–2*, *2–3*, *3–4*, *4–0* along the stretchout. Draw vertical lines of any length from these points in the stretchout. Project lines from the points on the front view to intersect the corresponding vertical lines. Connect the points of intersection with straight lines.

Rectangular 90° Duct Elbow

Draw the right angle *ABC*, Layout 13. With *B* as a center, draw arc *AC* to represent the outer curve or *heel* of the elbow. With *B* as a center, draw arc *DE* to represent the inner curve or *throat* of the elbow. Add straight sections *CF*, *EG*, *DH*, and *AI* to the curve. The straight parts are added to

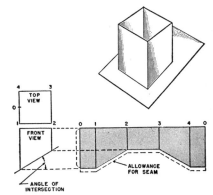

12. Laying out a pattern for square and rectangular intersections.

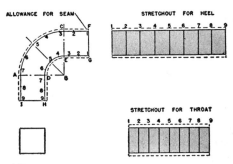

13. Laying out a pattern for a rectangular 90° duct elbow.

make an easy connection with the straight duct.

The stretchouts for the heel and throat are simply two rectangular pieces. The true lengths of these pieces may be found by dividing curves *FI* and *GH* into any number of equal parts and then laying out these parts in a horizontal line as shown in Layout 13.

How To Make Pattern Drawings 147

Transition of Rectangular to Round Section

Draw a front and top view as shown in Layout 14. Divide ¼ of the circle into any number of equal parts, such as four. From point C draw a line to each of the points on the circle, as line C1, C2, C3, C4.

Prepare a true length diagram by drawing horizontal line OP of indefinite length and vertical line CO equal in length to the height of the transition piece as shown in the front view. With 0 as a center and F4, C1, C2, C3, and C4 on the top view as radii, draw arcs intersecting the horizontal line OP at F, 1, 2, 3, and 4. Connect each of these points with C. These lines represent the true lengths of the corresponding lines in the top view.

To draw the half-pattern, first draw the horizontal line DC to represent the base. With D and C as centers and the true lengths CF, C4, C3, C2, and C1 as radii, draw arcs of indefinite lengths. With points 1, 2, 3, on the half-pattern as centers and distances 1–2, 2–3, 3–4 of the top view as radii, draw arcs intersecting arcs at D2, D3, D4 and C2, C3, C4. Then draw a curve through the intersecting arcs at points 4, 3, 2, 1, 2, 3, 4. Draw lines to connect D and 4, D and 1, C and 1, and C and 4.

Using D and C of the half-pattern as centers and CF of the top view as radius, draw arcs of indefinite lengths. With points 4 and 4 on the half-pattern as centers and the distance CF from the true length diagram as a ra-

dius, draw arcs to intersect arcs at E and F. Then draw straight lines DE, E4, CF, and F4. This completes the outline of the half-pattern. The usual practice in sheetmetal development is to prepare only a half-pattern for symmetrical objects. By turning the half-pattern over, using 4F or 4E as the hinge, the opposite half can be traced.

14. Laying out a pattern for rectangular to round section.

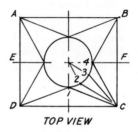

TOP VIEW

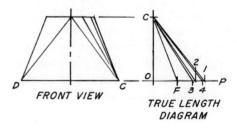

FRONT VIEW   TRUE LENGTH DIAGRAM

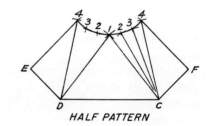

HALF PATTERN

PROBLEMS

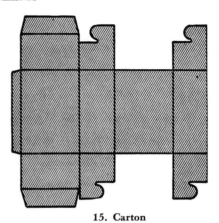

1. Design a Carton similar to Drawing 15 so it will be 2⅜″ deep, 4″ wide, and 5½″ long. Lay out the pattern on heavy drawing paper, cut and fold into shape.

15. Carton

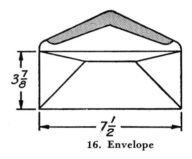

2. Design an Envelope as shown in Drawing 16. Cut out the pattern, fold and paste together to check your design.

$3\frac{7}{8}$ $7\frac{1}{2}$

16. Envelope

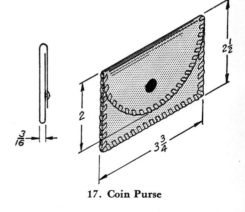

3. Lay out a pattern for a Coin Purse similar to Drawing 17. Use any desired size.

$\frac{3}{16}$ 2 $2\frac{1}{2}$ $3\frac{3}{4}$

17. Coin Purse

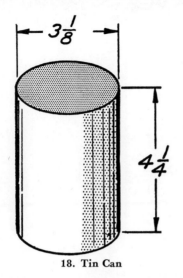

18. Tin Can

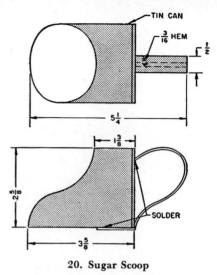

20. Sugar Scoop

4. Lay out a pattern for the Tin Can shown in Drawing 18. Include bottom. Paste pieces together.

6. Lay out the pattern for the Sugar Scoop shown in Drawing 20.

5. Lay out the patterns for the Tin Cup shown in Drawing 19.

7. Lay out the pattern for the Brooder Canopy shown in Drawing 21. Use any convenient scale. Allow for a ¼″ hem on the bottom.

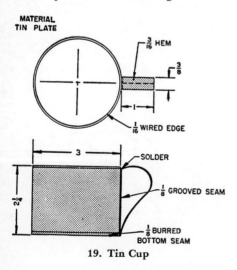

19. Tin Cup

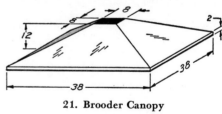

21. Brooder Canopy

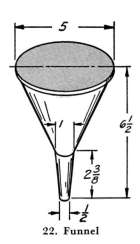

22. Funnel

8. Lay out the patterns for the Funnel shown in Drawing 22. Cut out and fasten pieces together.

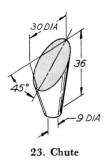

23. Chute

9. Produce a scaled pattern for the Chute shown in Drawing 23.

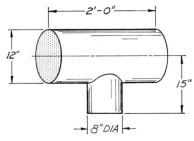

24. Intersecting Cylinders

10. Develop the surfaces of the Intersecting Cylinders shown in Drawing 24. Use any convenient scale and fasten pieces together.

How To Make Pattern Drawings **151**

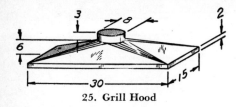

25. Grill Hood

11. Make a scaled pattern of the Grill Hood shown in Drawing 25. Allow for hems and seams where needed.

12. Lay out the pattern for the Tool Box and Tray shown in Drawing 26.

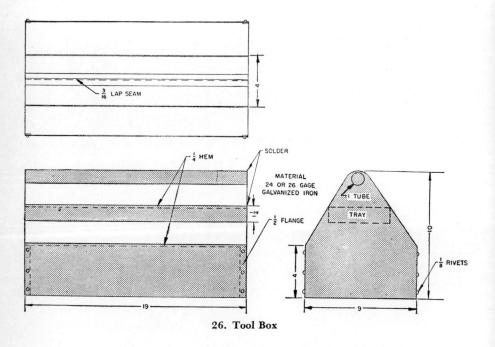

26. Tool Box

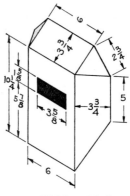

4

$\frac{1}{4}$ LAP SEAM

4

26 OR 28 GAGE
GALVANIZED IRON
SOLDER ALL SEAMS

13. Lay out the pattern for the Flower Container shown in Drawing 27.

$\frac{1}{4}$ HEM

$\frac{1}{4}$ LAP SEAM

4

$3\frac{1}{2}$

27. Flower Container

14. Lay out the pattern for the part of a Welder's Mask, shown in Drawing 28.

28. Welder's Mask

How To Make Pattern Drawings **153**

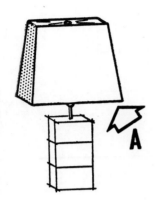

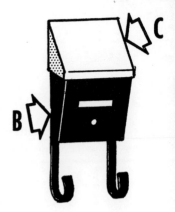

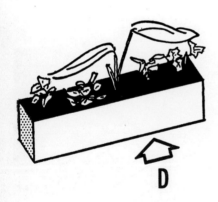

1. Make a freehand pattern of the articles shown in A, B, and C. Assume any desired sizes.

2. If the flower box shown in D was 5″ wide, 4″ high and 12″ long, how much material would be needed to make it?

3. What would be the shape of the pattern for the pail shown in E?

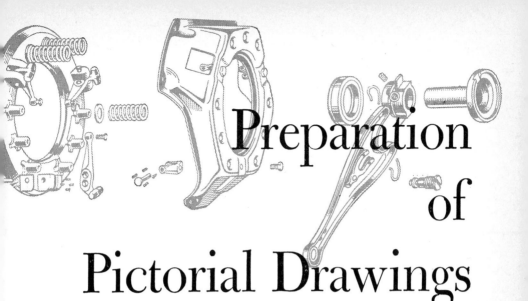

Preparation of Pictorial Drawings

Although a working drawing does show the exact shape of an object, such a drawing is usually of value only to the person who understands drafting principles. Consequently, multi-view drawings are employed primarily by shopmen, draftsmen, engineers, and construction workers.

There will be instances when an object must be illustrated to someone who is not familiar with conventional drawing techniques. For this purpose, a draftsman uses a form of drawing known as pictorial drawing. See Photograph 1. There are three principal types of pictorial drawings—*isometric*, *oblique*, and *perspective*. In this unit you will find how various pictorial drawings are made.

1. Here you see a draftsman preparing a pictorial drawing.

Courtesy Ford Motor Co.

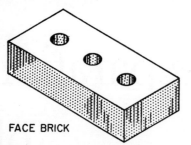

FACE BRICK

2. This is an example of an isometric drawing.

Isometric Drawing

An isometric drawing is one which clearly shows three surfaces of an object. See Drawing 2. The drawing consists of three axes, one of which is vertical and the other two drawn to the right and left at an angle of 30° to the horizontal. See Illustration 3.

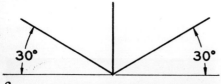

3. An isometric drawing is developed about three axes.

The object itself can be rotated so that either the right or left side is visible. See Illustration 4. Whether the object is drawn with its main surfaces extending to the right or left depends entirely upon which side is the most advantageous to show. Incidentally,

4. An isometric drawing can be slanted either to the right or left.

LEFT   RIGHT

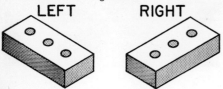

hidden lines are usually not included in a pictorial drawing.

To make an isometric drawing, proceed as follows:

1. Draw a vertical line. From the top or base of this line, extend two slanted lines at an angle of 30° to the horizontal. See A in Illustration 5.

2. Lay out the actual width, length, and height on these three lines. See B in Illustration 5. Complete each sur-

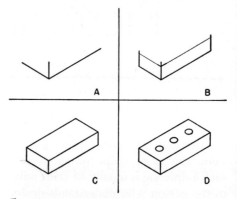

5. These are the steps in laying out an isometric drawing.

face by drawing the necessary lines parallel to the axes. See C. In isometric drawings, measurements are made only along the three isometric axes.

3. Proceed in this same manner to lay out and draw in the remaining details of the object. See D.

4. When an object has slanted lines that do not run parallel to the axes, these lines are called nonisometric lines. See Illustration 6. Since lines of this kind do not appear in their true lengths, they cannot be measured as regular isometric lines. Therefore, it

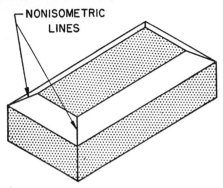

NONISOMETRIC
LINES

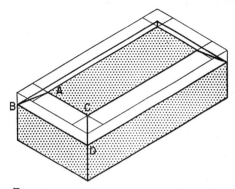

6. These lines are nonisometric lines.

7. How nonisometric lines are located.

is necessary to locate the extreme ends of these lines first. Once their end points are found, the slanted lines can easily be drawn. Thus, in Illustration 7, points *A, B, C* and *D* are located and then lines *AB* and *CD* drawn.

5. If the object has an irregular curve as shown in Layout 8, the curve can be constructed by drawing a series of isometric lines and the points plotted by measuring along these isometric lines.

8. Laying out an irregular curve on an isometric drawing. A French curve is used here.

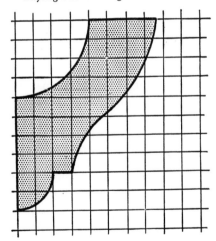

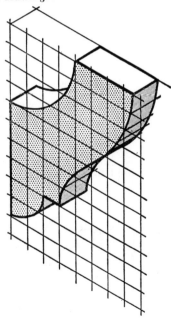

Preparation of Pictorial Drawings **157**

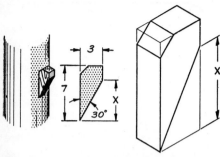

9. Laying out a nonisometric line having an angular measurement.

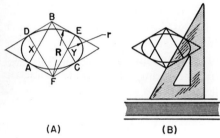

(A)   (B)

10. This is how an isometric circle is drawn.

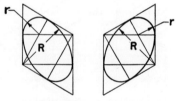

11. Isometric circles can be drawn to the right and left.

12. This is a sectional view in isometric.

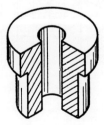

6. When a nonisometric line is indicated by an angular measurement, a partial view of the object is drawn as shown in Illustration 9. The actual dimensions of the line representing the angle are taken from this view and laid off on the isometric lines.

7. To draw an isometric circle or arc, construct an isometric square of the desired size. Find the center of each side of the square, and from these centers draw lines *AB, BC, DF,* and *EF.* See A in Construction 10. These same lines can be drawn by means of a 60° triangle as shown in B of Construction 10. With *r* as a radius, and *X* and *Y* as centers, draw arcs *EC* and *AD.* With *R* as a radius and *B* and *F* as centers, construct arcs *DE* and *AC.* To draw circles on the right or left surfaces of the object, study Construction 11.

8. Sometimes it is necessary to draw an isometric sectional view. Drawing 12 illustrates the standard practice for making such views. The section lines should be drawn at an angle that produces the most pleasing effect. However, they should never be drawn parallel to object-lines.

Oblique Drawing

The oblique drawing resembles an isometric except that one face of the object is parallel to the plane of projection. As in isometric drawings there are 3 axes. Two of these are at 90° to each other and the third is generally 30° or 45°. See Drawing 13. The procedure for constructing an oblique is the same as in making an isometric.

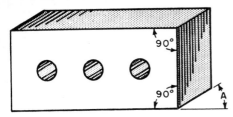

13. This is an oblique drawing. Notice how it differs from an isometric drawing. Angle A is generally 30° or 45°

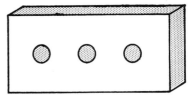

15. This is an example of a cabinet drawing.

ing lines have been foreshortened one-half their actual distance. See Drawing 15. This is done to reduce the distortion that is frequently evident on some regular oblique and isometric drawings. See Illustration 16.

Perspective Drawing

A perspective drawing is one which more nearly presents an object as it appears to the eye or as seen in an actual picture. This type of drawing is used more frequently by architectural draftsmen and artists than by other draftsmen or engineers.

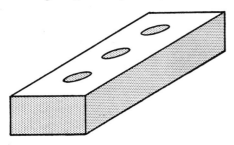

14. Selection of the smaller surface as the front face gives a less pleasing appearance, and in this case necessitates the tedious job of making elliptical shapes on a receding surface as shown in 14A.

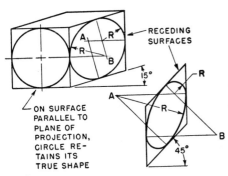

16. Today cabinet drawings are used for other materials besides wood.

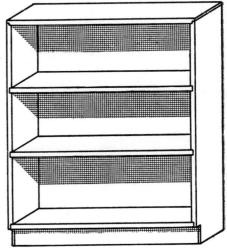

14A. To make four-center ovals, points A and B are found by drawing lines at the midpoints of the sides perpendicular to the sides. At 30° the construction shown in Fig. 11 may be used.

Cabinet Drawing

A cabinet drawing is actually an oblique drawing except that the reced-

17. This is an example of a perspective drawing.

Perspective drawing is based on the fact that all lines which extend from the observer appear to converge or draw together at some distant point. For example, to a person sighting down a long stretch of highway, light poles and wires and buildings will appear to slant and run together as shown in Picture 17. The point where all lines seem to meet is known as the *vanishing point*. This vanishing point is located on the horizon, which is an imaginary line in the distance and at eye level. All lines below eye level have the appearance of rising upward to the horizon, and all lines above eye level appear to go downward to the horizon. The object can be drawn so the vanishing point is either to the left or to the right, or directly in the center of vision. See Illustration 18.

Some perspective drawings may have two vanishing points. When a

18. These are the positions of the vanishing point in perspective drawings. In perspective drawing, objects are represented as they appear.

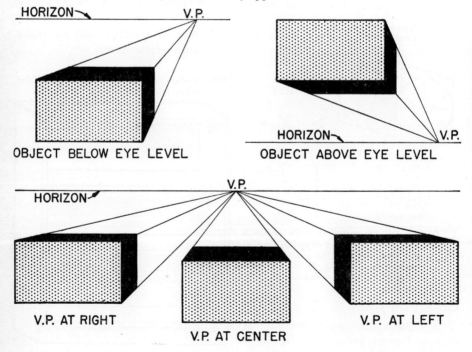

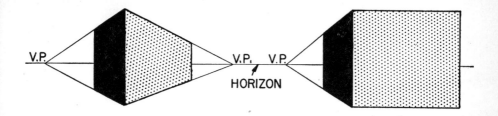

ANGULAR PERSPECTIVE   PARALLEL PERSPECTIVE

19. Notice the location of the vanishing points for the angular and parallel perspective drawings.

drawing is made with one vanishing point, it is said to be drawn in *parallel* perspective. A drawing with two vanishing points is known as an *angular* perspective. See Illustration 19.

To make a simple perspective drawing or sketch, proceed as follows:

1. Assume the location of the horizon line.

2. Locate the position of the vanishing points.

3. For a parallel perspective, draw a front view of the object. This will be a true view. See Construction 20. If

an angular perspective is to be made, draw a vertical line and on it, lay off the full or scaled height of the object. See Construction 21.

4. From the front view or vertical line, draw light construction lines back toward the vanishing points.

5. The points designating the length or depth of the object may be found by a projection method. However, since this is a complicated procedure, it is used only when an accurate mechanical perspective is made. For most purposes, location points for

20. Making a parallel perspective drawing.

21. Making an angular perspective drawing.

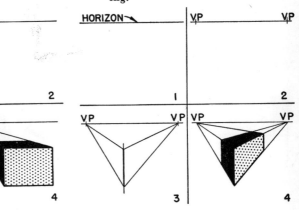

depth are simply assumed, that is, the vertical lines representing the ends of the object are placed in a position that produces the most pleasing effect.

6. Darken in all outlines. Surfaces that lie in a shaded area may be lightly shaded.

SHADING

One of the main purposes of a pictorial drawing is to achieve better visualization of an object. It is a means of bridging the gap between an actual photograph and the natural object. To make a pictorial drawing appear more natural, a process of shading is often used. Shading is simply a technique of varying the light intensity on the surfaces by lines or tones. Notice in Illustration 22 how shading helps to better visualize the shape of the object.

Location of Shaded Areas

Since shading is a result of light intensity on a surface, the first consideration in producing a shaded effect is to determine the source of light falling on the object. Generally speaking, one can proceed on the basis that the principal source of light is shining over the observer's left shoulder or from the upper corner of the drafting board, as shown in Illustration 23. This, however, is not necessarily a fixed rule

22. Shading aids the imagination in visualizing the shape of the object.

23. Direction of the main source of light falling on an object.

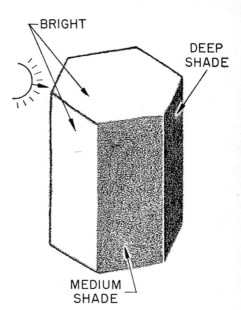

24. How the standard direction of light affects the surfaces of an object.

since sources of light from other directions may often produce an even more pleasing appearance. However, if we assume that the standard direction of light is over the left shoulder, then the top and front surfaces of the object receive the most light. The sides that form the smallest angle with the light rays have less light, and the surfaces that are directly opposite the light source are in deep shade (Illustration 24).

By following this rule, shading can be accomplished by sketching contrasting weights of lines over the surfaces affected by the light. It is well to keep in mind, too, that a more pleasing effect can be obtained by having the shaded area of one plane adjacent to the light area of an adjoining surface (Illustration 25).

Before actually proceeding with any shading, it is good practice to outline with a very fine line the areas that are to be shaded. The line should be light enough so it can be erased after the shading is completed (Illustration 26).

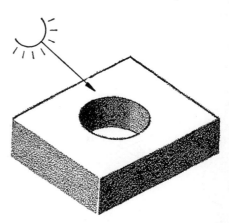

25. Place a shaded area adjacent to a light area.

Line Shading

The simplest method of producing shading effects is by means of contrasting weights and spacing of lines.

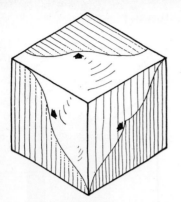

26. Sketch the outline of the shaded areas with a fine line.

Illustration 27 shows how such lines are sketched on flat surfaces. The spacing of lines should be judged by eye. Notice that the darker the area, the closer will be the lines. Actually no hard and fast rule can be given as to the amount of space to leave between lines. Practice and judgment will serve as the best guide. The point to keep in mind is to visualize the intensity of light cast on the object and

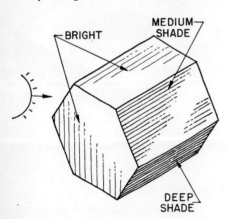

27. This shows line shading on flat surfaces.

then space the lines so they will best reflect the effects of this light.

The weight of lines can be achieved by varying the pressure on the pencil. Notice in Illustration 27 that the heaviest lines are used where the surface is to have the darkest areas. It is also possible to produce shaded effects by keeping all the lines light and varying the spacing (Illustration 28). As a

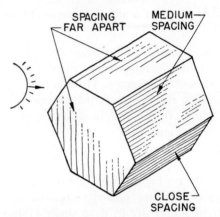

28. Shading can be produced by varying the spacing of lines.

rule, better results will be achieved by varying both the spacing and weight of lines. The direction of the lines must also be taken into consideration. Usually, it is best to shade vertical faces with vertical lines and the other faces with lines parallel to one of the edges of the object (Illustration 29).

To shade curved surfaces, the lines may be sketched straight or curved. The practice is to shade approximately one-fifth of the surface nearest the source of light, then leave the next two-fifths white and shade the two-fifths that are the farthest from the

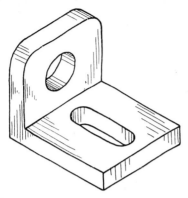

29. This shows the direction of lines for the best shading effects.

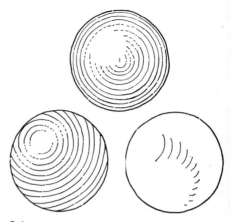

31. This is how to shade a sphere.

light (Illustration 30). Spheres are shaded by sketching a series of concentric circles, as demonstrated in Illustration 31.

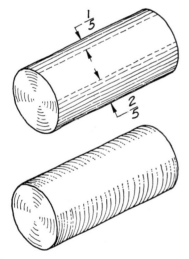

30. This is how a curved surface can be shaded.

Stippling

Stippling is another method which can be used to produce shaded areas. This method consists of covering the surface to be shaded with a series of dots made with the point of the pencil. For dark areas, the dots are placed closer together, and for light areas the dots are spaced widely apart (Illustration 32). Although stippling produces a pleasing appearance, the process is much slower than line shading.

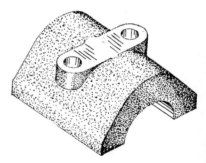

32. Shaded areas can be achieved by stippling.

Broad Stroke and Smudge Shading

Good shading results can be achieved by rubbing the desired areas

Preparation of Pictorial Drawings **165**

with the flattened side of the lead pencil (Illustration 33).

If a smudge effect is desired, as shown in Illustration 34, the broad pencil strokes should be rubbed with a paper stump. Once the area is covered, light and dark effects can be achieved by placing an erasing shield over the shaded part and rubbing with an eraser (Illustration 35).

BROAD STROKE   **SMUDGE**

34. This is an example of smudge shading.

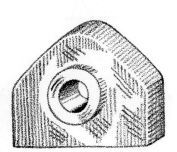

33. This is an example of broad stroke shading.

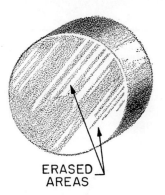

ERASED AREAS

35. Erasing in a shaded area produces light spots.

SELF QUIZ

1. Of what value are pictorial drawings?

2. In an isometric drawing, at what angle are the axes constructed?

3. When making a pictorial drawing, what determines whether the object should be slanted to the right or left?

4. What are nonisometric lines?

5. How does an oblique drawing differ from an isometric?

6. What is meant by a cabinet drawing?

7. When is this type of pictorial drawing used?

8. What is meant by a perspective drawing?

9. In a perspective drawing, where should the vanishing point be located in reference to the horizon?

10. What is the difference between an angular and parallel perspective drawing?

11. Why is shading often used in making pictorial drawings?

12. In order to achieve effective shading, what factor must always be considered, regardless of the technique being used?

13. What methods may be used in shading curved surfaces?

14. What is meant by line shading?

15. How is stippling done in shading an object?

16. What is meant by smudge shading?

PROBLEMS

1. Design a novelty Christmas Tree using the basic sizes shown in Drawing 36. Construct a cabinet drawing to a convenient scale.

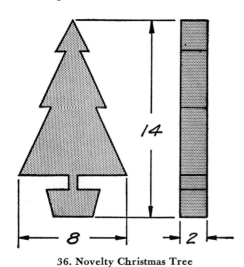

36. Novelty Christmas Tree

2. Construct a full-size cabinet drawing of the Hockey Puck shown in Drawing 37.

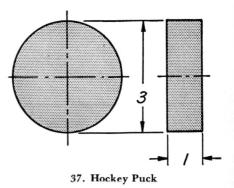

37. Hockey Puck

3. Make an isometric drawing of the Saw Horse shown in Drawing 38.

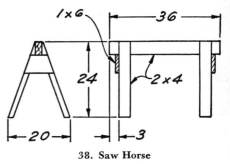

38. Saw Horse

Preparation of Pictorial Drawings **167**

4. Construct a scaled isometric drawing of the Chimney Block shown in Drawing 39.

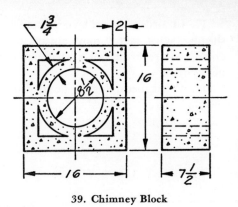

39. Chimney Block

5. Construct a cabinet drawing of the Bobsled Runner shown in Layout 40. Material is 1½″ thick. Select suitable scale.

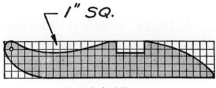

40. Bobsled Runner

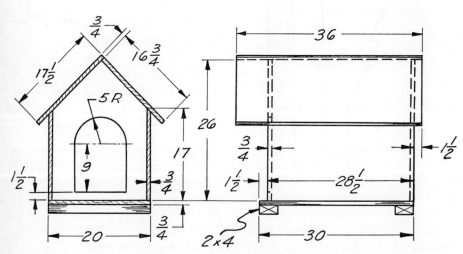

6. Make an isometric drawing of the Dog House shown in the above drawing.

7. Construct a parallel perspective drawing of the plastic Knife and Fork Tray shown in Drawing 42. Choose convenient locations for horizon and vanishing points.

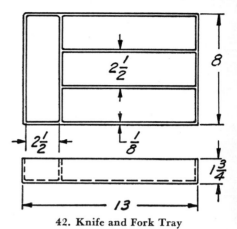

8. Construct an isometric drawing of the Child's Step Stool shown in Drawing 43.

42. Knife and Fork Tray

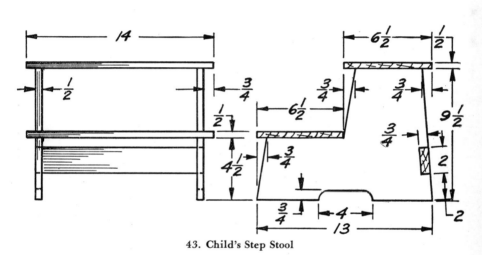

43. Child's Step Stool

9. Construct an angular perspective drawing of the Step End Table shown in Drawing 44. Assume convenient location of horizon and vanishing points.

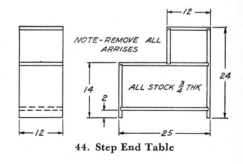

NOTE - REMOVE ALL ARRISES

ALL STOCK $\frac{3}{4}$ THK

44. Step End Table

10. Make a pictorial drawing of the fixture shown in Illustration 45 and shade it. Use your own dimensions.

11. Make a pictorial drawing of the fitting shown in Illustration 46 and shade it. Use any convenient dimensions.

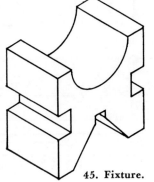

45. Fixture.

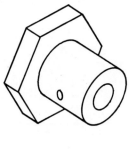

46. Fitting.

PICTORIAL QUIZ

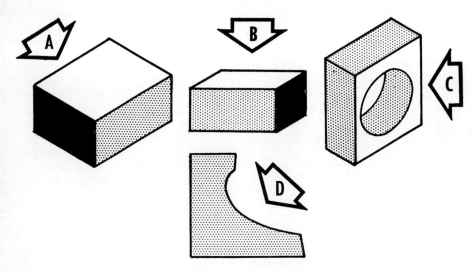

1. What type of pictorial drawing is shown at A?

2. What type of pictorial drawing is shown at B? How does it differ from A?

3. Where must the radius points be located for drawing the circle on Drawing C?

4. What is the procedure for drawing the irregular curve at D in isometric?

Drawing Without Instruments

UNIT 13

Freehand sketching is a process of producing a drawing without the aid of instruments. This type of drawing is often used by draftsmen, engineers, designers, and shopmen to illustrate ideas, or to make preliminary plans or "hurry-up" drawings of objects which later are to be manufactured. In fact, most articles that are made are usually sketched freehand first in order to get a general picture of their shape or design. Once the idea or design is accepted, then accurate mechanical drawings are produced. The sketch may be pictorial, such as perspective, isometric, cabinet, or it may be a multi-view drawing. The purpose of this unit is to give you an opportunity to study some of the basic principles used in making freehand sketches.

Cross-Section Paper

In learning to make freehand sketches, it is much better to use cross-section paper since this paper makes it possible to secure correct proportions. Thus, the squares on the paper can be

1. Sketching on cross-section paper.

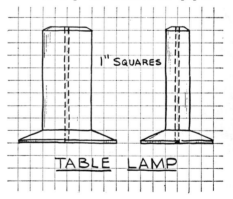

1" SQUARES

TABLE LAMP

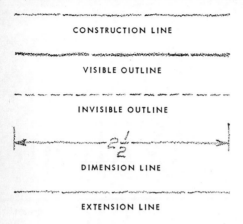

CONSTRUCTION LINE

VISIBLE OUTLINE

INVISIBLE OUTLINE

$2\frac{1}{2}$

DIMENSION LINE

EXTENSION LINE

CENTER LINE

2. Weight of lines for freehand sketching.

used to represent certain sizes; and by counting either horizontally or vertically, the right shape of the object can readily be sketched. For example, if the paper is ruled in $\frac{1}{4}''$ squares, each square can be used to represent $\frac{1}{8}''$, $\frac{1}{4}''$, $\frac{1}{2}''$, or $1''$, or any other size unit which you may find convenient. See Sketch 1. Moreover, the ruled lines will serve as guides in sketching lines.

3. These are the directions for sketching lines.

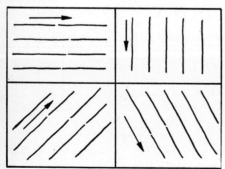

Pencil

A pencil with a soft lead is best for making freehand sketches. A grade F or H pencil is recommended. The point of the pencil should be sharpened to a long, conical shape. The pencil should be held loosely and approximately $1''$ to $1\frac{1}{2}''$ above the point.

When drawing straight or curved lines, it is advisable to pull rather than to push the pencil. Pushing a pencil may cause the point to catch the surface of the paper and puncture or tear it. As the pencil is pulled, it is a good practice to rotate it slightly, since this motion keeps the point sharper for a longer period. When the line begins to widen, it is a sign that the pencil needs resharpening.

Types of Lines

In general, the same kinds of lines are used for freehand sketching that are used for mechanical drawings. A line to represent visible edges must be quite heavy and very black. Invisible

4. Turn the paper at an angle for drawing freehand lines.

lines to show unseen edges should also be very black. Dimension and center lines need to be finer, and construction lines very light. See Illustration 2. The width and darkness of lines can be regulated by varying the pressure on the pencil.

Sketching Straight Lines

To sketch a horizontal line, move the pencil from left to right. Start a vertical line at the top and sketch it downward. See Illustration 3. An inclined line should be sketched from left to right. However, it is often more convenient to turn the paper at an angle when sketching straight lines. See Illustration 4.

When sketching straight lines, start by marking the end points with dots or small crosses. Then sketch a very light trial line between the points. Keep the eyes on the point toward which the line is being drawn. If the line is long so that it cannot be sketched in a single stroke, it is better to draw several short lines of about 1½″ to 2″ in length. Use a free arm motion, avoiding as much as possible finger and wrist movement. By turning the paper at an angle, the arm can be held away from the body to permit a more free arm-motion. After light trial lines are sketched and appear to be satisfactory, trace over the lines and darken them.

Sketching Circles

To sketch a circle, first lay out vertical and horizontal center lines equal to the diameter of the desired circle. Through these outer points, sketch

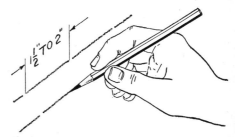

5. To sketch a long line, use several short strokes.

lines to form a square. Next sketch lines to connect the four center points on the sides of the square to form small triangles. Make a point in the center of each triangle and, starting from one corner of the triangle, sketch an arc through this center mark and over to the next corner of the triangle. Repeat this procedure for the other three triangles. See Construction 6.

Another method which may be used to construct a circle is to sketch a vertical and a horizontal line and several diagonal lines. The radius of the circle is then marked on these lines, and short arcs are drawn through these points. See Construction 7.

Sketching a Working Drawing

As you learned in Unit 7, a working drawing may consist of one or

6. This is the procedure for sketching circles.

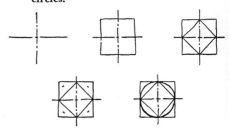

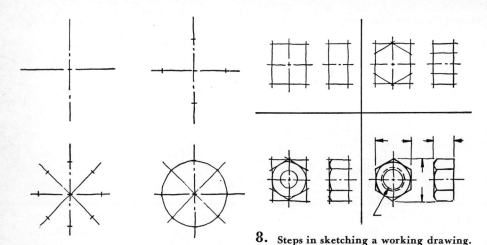

7. Another method for sketching circles.

8. Steps in sketching a working drawing.

more views. The actual procedure for sketching these views is the same as for making a regular instrument draw-ing, except that all lines are made free-hand. In other words, the number and position of the views remain the same.

9. The steps in sketching a pictorial drawing are the same as when instruments are used.

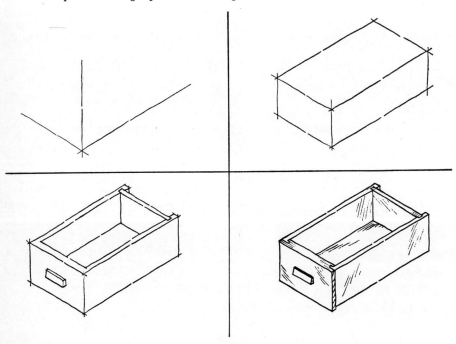

To sketch a working drawing, the usual practice is to block in each view with light construction lines. After the necessary details are added, darken all lines and insert the required dimensions. See Illustration 8.

How To Sketch Pictorial Drawings

It was pointed out in Unit 11 that all draftsmen should know how to make pictorial drawings. As a matter of fact, a draftsman will have more occasion to produce a pictorial drawing by freehand sketching than by mechanical means.

It is obvious, of course, that the principles involved in sketching freehand isometric, oblique, or perspective drawings are the same as those used in making an accurate drawing with instruments. See Unit 11. After the proper front plane of the object is selected, the various surfaces are sketched in lightly. Essential details are added and then all lines are darkened. See Illustration 9.

SELF QUIZ

1. Is there any particular value in being able to make freehand sketches?
2. In learning to make freehand sketches, why should cross-section paper be used?
3. What grade pencil should be used in freehand sketching?
4. In which direction should the pencil be moved in sketching horizontal lines?
5. How should vertical and slanted lines be sketched?
6. What is the best procedure to follow in sketching long lines?
7. Show by means of a sketch how to draw a circle.
8. When sketching an object, what determines how many views should be shown?
9. Of what value are pictorial sketches?
10. In an isometric sketch, how many surfaces are visible? Explain.
11. How does an oblique sketch differ from an isometric sketch?
12. When making an oblique sketch, what can be done to avoid distorting the view?
13. How does a perspective sketch differ from an oblique sketch?
14. For a perspective sketch, in which direction may the receding lines be slanted?
15. Look through some current magazines and locate some examples of sketches used in advertisements or as illustrations for articles.
16. List the time during the last twenty-four hours when you could have used a sketch to express your ideas better.
17. Outline briefly the values of sketching for a factory foreman or a business executive.

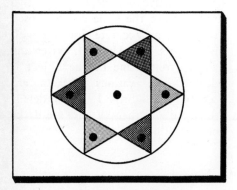

10. Ring Toss Game Board

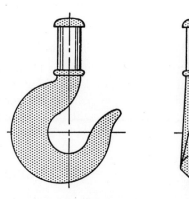

12. Crane Hook

1. Make a freehand layout sketch of the Ring Toss Game Board shown in Drawing 10.

2. Make a freehand dimensioned multi-view sketch of the Miter Box shown in Drawing 11.

3. Make a two-view sketch of the Crane Hook shown in Drawing 12. Use any desired size.

4. Make a three-view dimensioned sketch of the Steel Bench Stop shown in Drawing 13.

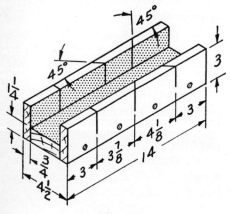

11. Miter Box

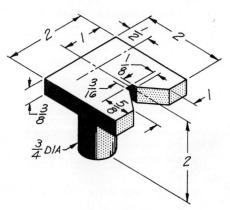

13. Bench Stop

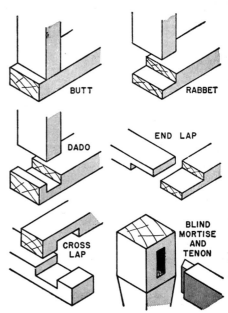

14. Woodworking Joints

5. Make pictorial sketches of the Woodworking Joints shown in Illustration 14.

6. Sketch pictorially the Roller Chain Link shown in Drawing 15. Show all dimensions.

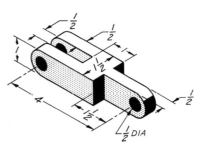

15. Roller Chain Link

7. Make a multi-view sketch of the Wall Shelf shown in Drawing 16. Use any convenient scale and show all dimensions.

8. Make a freehand working drawing of any of the problems in Unit 7.

9. Make a freehand pictorial drawing of any of the problems in Unit 11.

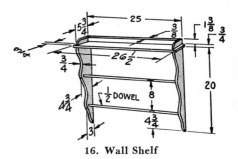

16. Wall Shelf

PICTORIAL QUIZ

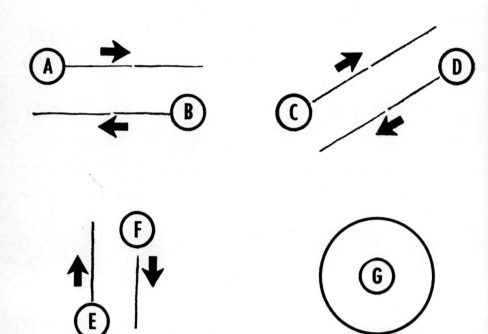

1. In sketching horizontal lines, should they be drawn as in A or B?

2. Which is correct, C or D?

3. Should vertical lines be drawn as in E or F?

4. Show how you would sketch the circle in G freehand.

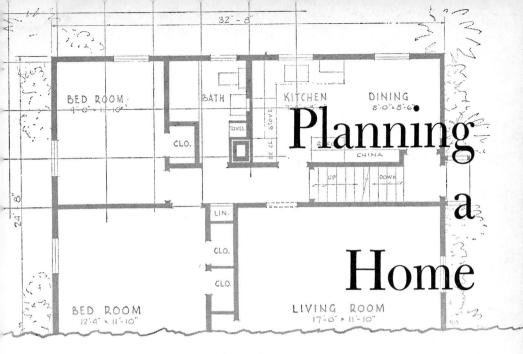

Planning a Home

UNIT 14

At some time or other many of you will be thinking about building a home. Although there are many agencies that will provide the necessary advice as to how one should proceed in planning a home, in all probability you will be able to plan better the type of home you actually need if you understand a few basic principles of home planning. Furthermore, a knowledge of these principles will help you explain more clearly and intelligently to the architect just what you want. In addition, there may at various times be remodeling jobs around your own home. Alterations to a room, a new sun porch, or perhaps an addition to the garage for storage of tools and furniture. Very often you will wish to do these jobs yourself in your spare time. One can readily see the value of knowing how to plan and read construction drawings at such times.

Moreover, a good knowledge of building terms and ability to understand architectural drawings and sketches is essential to persons engaged in various occupations. For example, the sales and office personnel at your local lumber dealers, hardware stores, and home service sections of the large department stores. In addition, the plumber, electrician, sheetmetal worker and roofer, heating and air conditioning man, mason, and, above all, the carpenter depend upon knowing how to interpret architectural drawings for their livelihood.

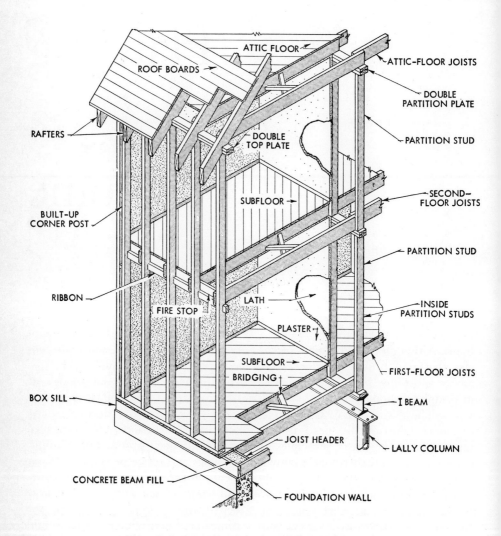

ATTIC FLOOR

ROOF BOARDS

ATTIC-FLOOR JOISTS

DOUBLE
PARTITION PLATE

PARTITION STUD

RAFTERS

DOUBLE
TOP PLATE

SUBFLOOR

SECOND-
FLOOR JOISTS

BUILT-UP
CORNER POST

PARTITION STUD

RIBBON

LATH

INSIDE
PARTITION STUDS

FIRE STOP

PLASTER

SUBFLOOR

FIRST-FLOOR JOISTS

BRIDGING

BOX SILL

I BEAM

JOIST HEADER

LALLY COLUMN

CONCRETE BEAM FILL

FOUNDATION WALL

1A. Common building terms are illustrated above.

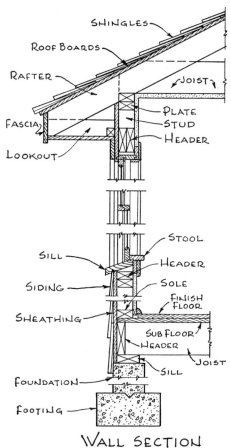

SHINGLES

ROOF BOARDS

RAFTER

FASCIA

LOOKOUT

PLATE

STUD

HEADER

JOIST

STOOL

SILL

HEADER

SIDING

SOLE

FINISH FLOOR

SHEATHING

SUB FLOOR

HEADER

JOIST

SILL

FOUNDATION

FOOTING

WALL SECTION

1B. This is a section through a house wall.

Common Building Terms

Before proceeding with an explanation of the basic principles of home planning, you should become familiar with a few common terms.

Types of House Architecture

Most houses being built today fall into two general classifications—*modernistic* and *traditional*. Designs of tra-

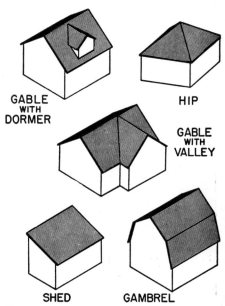

GABLE WITH DORMER

HIP

GABLE WITH VALLEY

SHED

GAMBREL

2. These are types of roofs commonly found on American houses.

ditional homes are based on a definite architectural style which existed in Europe or America during some historical period. Modernistic houses represent a radical departure from historical influences and have been developed by a group of architects who have cast aside tradition. They believe that the exterior appearance of a house need not necessarily be in keeping with some predetermined style of architecture. Rather, they have said, the interior requirements of the home owner are the primary consideration. Originally, modernistic homes were looked upon with some degree of skepticism, but because of their unusual adaptability for comfortable living, this viewpoint has gradually been dispelled.

Modernistic Style

It is difficult and perhaps unnecessary to classify modernistic homes into specific types. Their principal characteristic is their appearance, which differs radically from that of most conventional buildings. Some have flat roofs with numerous windows, which are, in some instances, continuous

4. A Frank Lloyd Wright home. These homes may differ greatly in appearance from traditional designs.

Courtesy Portland Cement Co.

3. This is a type of modernistic home. In the design of modern homes, emphasis is placed on comfort and convenience.

around the corners. See Photograph 3. Others, particularly those designed by Frank Lloyd Wright, depart from square or rectangular outlines and have curved walls. See Photograph 4.

The most popular in recent years has been the Ranch type house. See Photographs 5 and 6. This group of modernistic homes has a long, low appearance with a low-pitched roof. All the rooms are arranged on one floor. Often they have no basements, and living and dining rooms are combined. Large picture windows are used to achieve an atmosphere of outdoor living.

Traditional Style

As was mentioned previously, traditional homes are based on a type of architecture which prevailed in early historical periods. Although many of the designs have been modified through the years, in most instances certain features have been retained that still classify them as traditional architecture. The following are a few of the more common traditional homes:

English (Cotswold): Houses patterned after the Old English style are two or one and one-half story dwellings with steep, sloping roofs, and eaves located near the top of the first-floor windows. Quite often the roofs are covered with slate or clay tile. The buildings are picturesque and homelike in appearance. They have a spread-out look with large dormer windows and large chimneys. The large chimneys are in keeping with the original design of English homes where heating was entirely by means of fireplaces. The external walls are frequently built of rugged stone masonry and sometimes

Courtesy Harry A. Hurni, Builder

5. Ranch-type home. These homes have achieved great popularity in recent years because of their simple, practical design.

half-timbered designs are used. See Picture 7.

Elizabethan: The Elizabethan de-

sign has many of the features of the Old English architecture. Its unsymmetrical plan gives a very homelike

6. Ranch-type home. This type of home has only one story and often is constructed without a basement.

Courtesy Harry A. Hurni, Builder

Planning a Home 183

Courtesy Better Homes and Gardens

7. This house is based on Old English architecture.

and informal appearance. Some of its chief characteristics are prominent gables and high chimneys with extensive use of half-timbers on the exterior. See Photograph 8.

Courtesy Harry A. Hurni, Builder

8. Here is an Elizabethan style house.

Georgian: A Georgian styled house is usually full two stories in height with a low-hipped roof. Sometimes homes of this design have high-pitched gable roofs with large dormer windows. The house is either square or rectangular in shape. It is usually symmetrical and simple with no ornaments except for the entrance doorway and possibly the cornice. The external walls are covered with shingles or

siding, although brick is frequently used. See Picture 9.

Courtesy Better Homes and Gardens

9. A house based on Georgian architecture.

Dutch Colonial: The principal feature of the Dutch Colonial home is its gambrel roof. See Photograph 10. The building is one and one-half stories high but may be two or two and one-half stories high. One type has wide overhanging eaves whereas another has no overhanging eaves except for a narrow shelter over the entrance door. Some have either individual dormers or one continuous dormer. The first story is often built of stone and the second story of wood.

Southern Colonial: Homes of this type are easily recognized by their

10. A Dutch Colonial home has a gambrel roof.

Courtesy Better Homes and Gardens

wide verandas and massive columns extending up to the roof. These houses are large and are mostly found on plantations in many of the southern states. Their formal dignity is achieved by large and symmetrical doors and

12. The Cape Cod house is a traditional design that remains popular.

11. A Southern Colonial style house has a stately appearance.

windows. The walls are usually of brick and the slate roof is either hipped or gabled. See Photograph 11.

Cape Cod: The Cap Cod is one of the few traditional homes that is still very popular today. The building is either one or one and one-half stories. It has a rather steep pitched roof with several dormers. See Photograph 12. Sometimes a continuous dormer runs nearly the full length of the house. The windows have numerous small panes with shutters on each side. The exterior is covered with clapboard or shingles.

Regency: The Regency style home is another type of architecture which resulted from certain English influences. The current dwellings can be identified by their full two-story height with symmetrically spaced windows and shutters. Curved metal roofs

13. The Regency styled home displays English influences.

are found on the front and side entrances, and the exterior is usually of brick. See Picture 13.

Spanish: Houses of the Spanish design are found mostly in Florida and

14. A Spanish-type home is easily recognized.

southern California. They are easily recognized by their low-pitched, curved, red tile roofs, stucco walls, decorative balconies, wrought iron grilles, and courts called patios. See Picture 14.

Securing the Lot

When a person decides to build a home, one of his first problems is to secure a suitable lot. There are several factors which must be taken into consideration in buying the lot. Perhaps the most important is the selection of the right neighborhood. It would be foolish to build a house in a place where the existing dwellings will be entirely out of keeping with the style of the new home. Since the home-owner will probably live in the neighborhood for many years, he must be certain that he will be satisfied with the selected location. Furthermore, he should be sure that sufficient building restrictions are in force so in years to come his property will not depreciate in value because of inferior or undesirable structures built near by.

In selecting a lot, the buyer should take precautions that no swampy marshes are within the vicinity where clouds of mosquitoes may breed. Sites near railroads and heavily traveled highways should be avoided because of noises and vibrations. Equally important is the availability of adequate transportation, schools, and stores. There is also the matter of water, electricity, gas, sewers, and whether or not the roads are sufficiently main-tained for necessary travel. These latter items must be reckoned with, especially if the lot is outside the city limits. Building a house in an undeveloped section will require additional expense since a cesspool or septic tank must be installed and a well drilled for water.

Once a lot has been decided upon, it is necessary to check and see that the title is clear. In all probability, the land may have changed hands several times. During these transactions, some irregularities may have occurred which might affect the right of ownership. It is possible that even certain penalties have been attached to the property in the form of back taxes or road and sewer construction assessments. To protect himself, the buyer should insist on getting an *abstract*. This abstract will contain a complete history of all the transactions on the property. Before closing the deal, the buyer should have this abstract checked by some reputable attorney. In this way he can be assured that he will have a clear title to the property.

When the purchaser is certain that the abstract is in order he should have the seller furnish a *warranty deed*. A warranty deed is a document transferring ownership of the land. This deed should then be recorded with the designated governmental agency responsible for maintaining a record of all property in the community. Usually the financing agency handling the property loan takes care of such legal details as a service to clients.

Financing a Home

The great majority of home builders usually do not have enough funds to finance a home, so the practice is for them to borrow the money. A loan may be arranged either entirely through a private institution or under a government plan. Some people finance their homes by arranging a loan directly with a local bank or other financial organization. A system of repayment may be worked out which spreads monthly payments over a prescribed number of years. Regardless of the financing procedure followed, careful supervision is required to insure that the house is well built.

The Federal Government through the Federal Housing Administration has made it possible for people to secure easier terms. The FHA insures mortgage loans made by approved lending institutions. In this way, it is possible to borrow up to 95 per cent of the appraised value of a home at a rate of interest that is lower than can usually be obtained. Repayment is in monthly installments spread over a period that may extend up to thirty years. Payments include interest on the borrowed money, a portion of the principal borrowed, taxes, and insurance.

Many qualified veterans can have loans guaranteed by the Veterans' Administration. The VA plan enables a builder to borrow up to 100 per cent of the value of a home. Both the FHA and VA have specified certain minimum standards that must be met.

Determining What To Pay for a House

During the early planning stages, a person must decide on how much money he can afford to spend for a house. The generally accepted rule is that the total investment in a house should never exceed more than twice one's yearly income. For example, if a person has an income of $6,000 a year, the house he plans to build, including the cost of the lot, should not be more than $2 \times \$6,000$ or $12,000.

Determining the Size of the House

After the amount to be spent has been decided, the next step is to determine the size of building that can be constructed for the money available. One simple way to do this is to select some prepared floor plan and then figure the square-foot area of the first floor. The area can be found by multiplying the total width of the floor plan by the length. A contractor or architect should then be contacted for the prevailing square-foot cost of new houses. Multiplying the square-foot area by the cost per square foot will provide a rough index of what the house will cost.

Plan 15 shows a floor arrangement that has an area of approximately 900 square feet. Assuming that the cost is $14 per square foot, the estimated price of this house would be:

$$900 \text{ sq. ft.} \times 14 = \$12,600.$$

Most builders use the cubic-foot method of arriving at the cost of a house. The cubic content is found by multiplying the width, the length, and the height of the building. This is how it works. Using $12,000 as the amount to be spent and assuming that the prevailing cubic-foot cost is 80 cents, the size of the dwelling must not exceed:

$$\frac{12,000 \times 100 \ (\text{cents})}{80 \ \text{cents}} = 15,000 \ \text{cu. ft.}$$

15. The floor plan of this house has an area of 900 square feet.

Dividing the cubic content by the average height of the building gives the approximate area of the first floor. The average height of the building is found by adding together the height of the basement, first floor, second floor, and roof. For rough estimating, it is often the practice to use 8'-6" for the basement height, 9' for the first floor, 8'-6" for the second floor, and 4' for the roof. These heights will vary to some extent depending on the type of house to be built. Another method that is frequently used to figure building

height is to add the distance from the bottom of the basement floor slab to the eave plus one-half the height of the roof.

With a total cubic foot content of 15,000 and the height of 30', the square-foot area will be:

$$\frac{15,000 \ \text{cu. ft.}}{30 \ \text{ft.}} = 500 \ \text{sq. ft.}$$

To keep within the price range of $12,000, the house must have a first-floor plan not to exceed 500 square feet, or an overall dimension not to be more than 20' x 25'.

To use another illustration of calculating the size house by the cubic-content method, let us take a single-story house without a basement that is to cost not more than $14,000. The computation would be as follows:

1. $\dfrac{\$14,000 \times 100 \ (\text{cents})}{80 \ \text{cents (cost per cu. ft.)}} = 17,500$ cubic feet
2. Average height $= 9'$ first floor and $4'$ roof $= 13'$
3. $\dfrac{17,500 \ \text{cubic feet}}{13 \ (\text{total height of building})} = 1,346$ square feet
4. At this stage it is necessary to decide on the number and sizes of the rooms needed. Assume that the required needs are:

Living room 12' x 20' = 240 square feet		
Dining room 12' x 14' = 168	"	"
Kitchen 10' x 14' = 140	"	"
Bathroom 6' x 8' = 48	"	"
Utility Room 12' x 16' = 192	"	"
Bedroom 10' x 12' = 120	"	"
Bedroom 10' x 12' = 120	"	"
Bedroom 12' x 14' = 168	"	"
Hall 6' x 8' = 48	"	"
Total area = 1,244 square feet		

From these figures it is evident that if the house is to be kept at a cost of

$14,000, the sizes of the rooms must be kept to these limiting dimensions.

It must be remembered that the square-foot or cubic content method of computation provides only a quick approximation of the probable cost of the house. This system simply gives the owner an idea of how big a house he can build for the money he can afford to spend. Final cost depends on many factors, such as kind of materials used, prevailing workers' wage rates, kind of heating system installed, type of plumbing, fixtures, etc. Despite these items, experienced contractors and architects can arrive at a fairly accurate cost for a building. In some communities the services of professional estimators are available. These people specialize in figuring the cost of dwellings.

Sketching the Floor Plan

After a person has decided on the type of home he can afford to build, he proceeds to make rough sketches of

16. This is a floor plan sketched on graph paper. Each square represents a definite measurement.

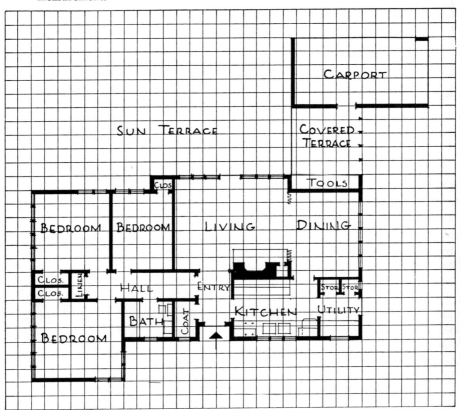

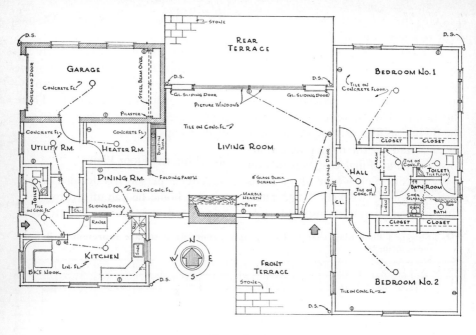

•FLOOR PLAN•

17. This is an accurate line drawing of a floor plan. Notice how symbols are used to indicate various features.

floor plans. Since he has already determined the number and square area of the rooms, the usual practice is to check several floor plans printed in magazines such as *Better Homes and Gardens* or other periodicals which feature floor plans and descriptions of homes.

In sketching floor plans, the use of squared or graph paper will greatly simplify the work. Each square of the paper can be made to represent a certain size such as six inches or one foot. Plan 16 illustrates a floor arrangement made on graph paper. By using this method it is possible to sketch a series of plans until the desired room ar-

rangements and areas are achieved.

People who have a knowledge of drawing practices very often will take the rough sketch and make a more accurate line drawing as shown in Plan 17. Notice that when preparing a line drawing, certain architectural conventions are used. A few of the more common symbols are given in Illustration 18.

Once the rough sketch or line drawing is completed, the next step is to consult a qualified architect. The architect will probably make certain suggestions and, when the details have been agreed upon, he will proceed to prepare a detailed set of plans. When

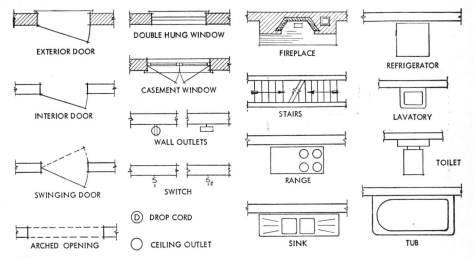

EXTERIOR DOOR

DOUBLE HUNG WINDOW

INTERIOR DOOR

CASEMENT WINDOW

FIREPLACE

REFRIGERATOR

STAIRS

WALL OUTLETS

LAVATORY

SWINGING DOOR

SWITCH

RANGE

TOILET

ARCHED OPENING

DROP CORD

CEILING OUTLET

SINK

TUB

18. These symbols are used in preparing floor plan drawings. The use of symbols helps to simplify drawings.

this is done, the final step is to hire a building contractor who assumes the responsibility for erecting the house according to the plans and specifications provided by the architect.

SELF QUIZ

1. Why should prospective home builders understand a few basic principles of home planning?

2. What is the difference between a hipped, gambrel, and gable roof?

3. How does modernistic architecture differ from the traditional architectural forms?

4. What are some of the identifying characteristics of Old English type houses?

5. What are some of the features of a Georgian type home?

6. What are the identifying features of a Cape Cod house?

7. What is the difference between a Southern Colonial house and a Dutch Colonial house?

8. What are the principal features of a Spanish type house?

9. Why is the Ranch type house so popular today?

10. What are some of the things one should consider in purchasing a lot?

11. What is the difference between an abstract and a deed?

12. What agency has been established by the Federal government to help people finance homes?

13. What should be the determining factor in deciding how much money to invest in a home?

14. What two methods are used in arriving at a rough estimate of the cost of a house?

PROBLEMS

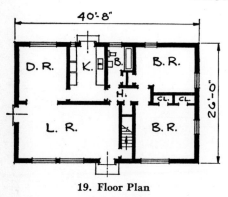

19. Floor Plan

1. Determine the square foot area of the Floor Plan shown in Illustration 19.

2. Determine the cubic content of the House shown in Illustration 20.

3. Check with an architect in your community for the cubic content cost and then figure the price of the House shown in Illustration 21.

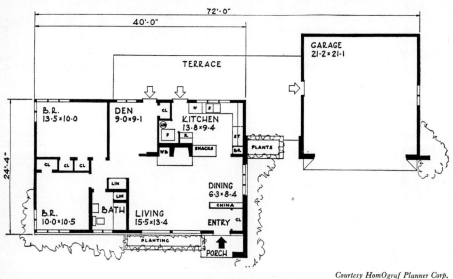

Courtesy HomOgraf Planner Corp.

20. House Plan

16'-0"

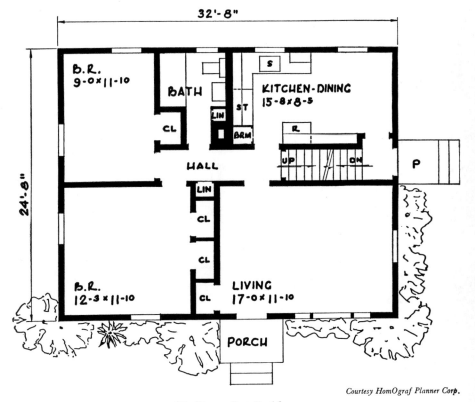

32'-8"

24'-8"

B.R.
9-0×11-10

BATH

CL

KITCHEN-DINING
15-8×8-5

S

ST

LIN

BRM

R

UP

DN

HALL

P

LIN

CL

CL

B.R.
12-3×11-10

LIVING
17-0×11-10

CL

PORCH

Courtesy HomOgraf Planner Corp.

21. House Cost Problem

4. Check with an architect in your community for the square foot cost and then figure the price of the House shown in Illustration 22.

5. Find a floor plan in a magazine and make a freehand drawing of it on graph paper, rearranging the rooms as you would like to have them for a home of your own.

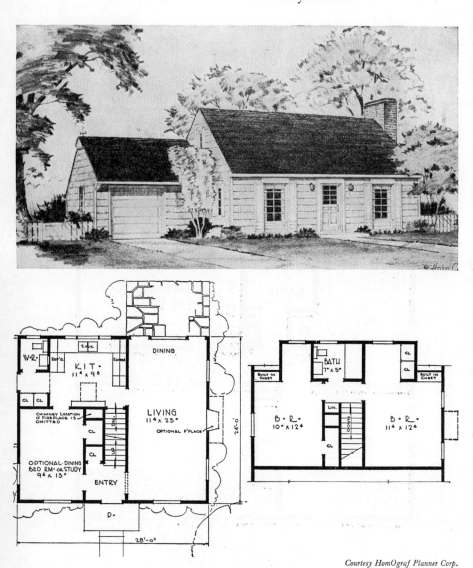

Courtesy HomOgraf Planner Corp.

22. House Cost Problem

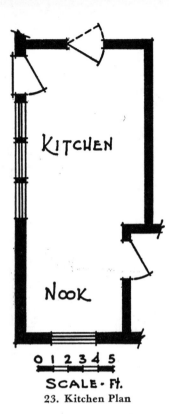

KITCHEN

NOOK

0 1 2 3 4 5
SCALE · Ft.
23. Kitchen Plan

6. Make an accurate drawing of the first floor of your home.

7. Using sizes from catalogs of plumbing supplies and kitchen equipment, place the desired equipment in a convenient arrangement for the Kitchen shown in Plan 23. Show electrical outlets where needed.

8. Make a floor plan and elevation drawing for a one-car garage having overall sizes as follows: 12'-0" wide by 20'-0" long. Use a commercial stock-size overhead door and any desired shape roof.

9. Assume that your yearly income is $6,200. Design a floor plan arrangement for a two-bedroom house that you can afford on this income.

PICTORIAL QUIZ

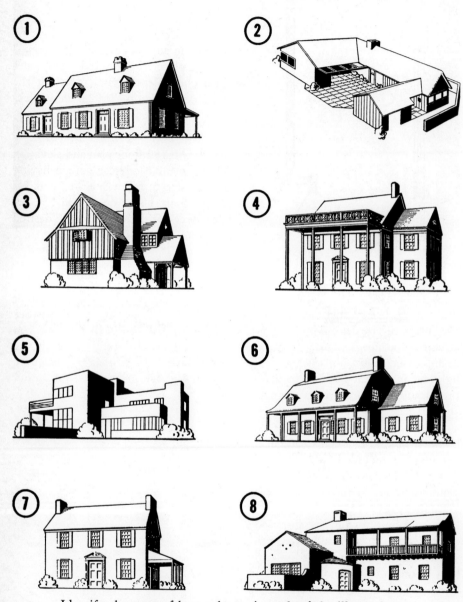

Identify the type of home shown in each of the illustrations.

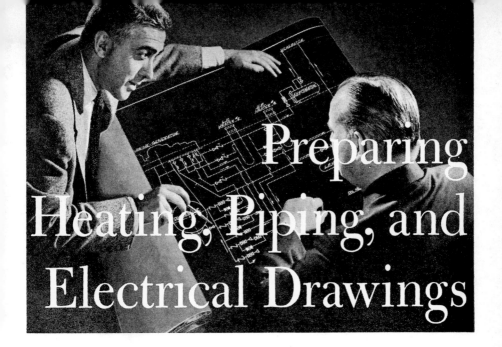

Preparing Heating, Piping, and Electrical Drawings

UNIT 15

A schematic, or diagrammatical drawing, as it is sometimes called, is used primarily for laying out electrical circuits, pipe lines, and duct work. For example, such a diagram may show the lighting arrangement for a house or the circuit for some electrical appliance. It may illustrate the wiring for a radio or a television set. When a house is designed, a schematic drawing may be included to indicate the water and sewer systems, and the complete layout of the ducts for the heating unit.

Schematic drawings are also used a great deal in aircraft and automotive work to show the layout of hydraulic lines, the control system, fuel and oil lines, the ignition system, and the hook-up for various gauges of engine performance. They are drawn either as flat layouts or in pictorial form. See Diagrams 1, 2 and 3. In this unit you will have the opportunity to study the procedures used in making the more common types of schematic drawings.

1. This is a schematic drawing of an aircraft fuel system.

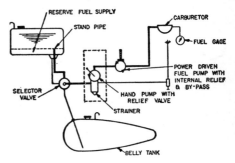

As a rule the draftsman is not required to have a detailed knowledge of piping design and piping specifications. The project engineer usually supplies the necessary information and preliminary flow sketch of the system. From this information and rough sketch the draftsman then prepares the finished drawing.

Although the draftsman is not expected to possess an extensive understanding of piping design, he should be familiar with basic piping knowledge so that he can intelligently prepare acceptable drawings. A brief discussion of a few elements of piping information is presented here. For more extensive details, texts on piping and plumbing should be consulted.

Piping and Tubing

The three basic standard weights of steel or wrought iron pipe are known as standard-weight, extra-strong and double extra-strong. For any given diameter, each of the three types has a different wall thickness but all have the same outside diameter. Up to 12 inches in diameter, steel pipe is classified by its nominal inside diameter. When reference is made to a specified diameter it does not mean that its size is actually as stated. Thus the inside diameter of a nominal 1″ standard-weight pipe is 1.049″, extra-strong is .957″ and double-extra strong is .599″. Pipe that is above 12″ in diameter is indicated by its outside diameter.

The required volume of flow usually governs the inside diameter of the pipe to be used. Wall thickness depends on such factors as internal pressure, external pressure and amount of expansion stresses encountered.

Extra-strong pipe is used mostly for steam, gas and hydraulics under high pressure. Double-extra strong is intended primarily for unusually high-pressure lines.

Cast iron pipe is designed for underground usage to carry gas, water or steam. Its high corrosion-resistance makes it particularly adaptable for this purpose. Its size is specified by the nominal inside diameter.

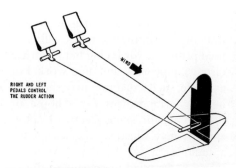

RIGHT AND LEFT
PEDALS CONTROL
THE RUDDER ACTION

WIND

2. An aircraft control system is here represented in schematic drawing.

Cast iron pipe is available either with flanged ends or with bell-and-spigot ends. The bell-and-spigot joint when properly calked and leaded makes a very tight connection especially for underground water lines. The pipe with a hub-and-spigot end is frequently used for gas and water

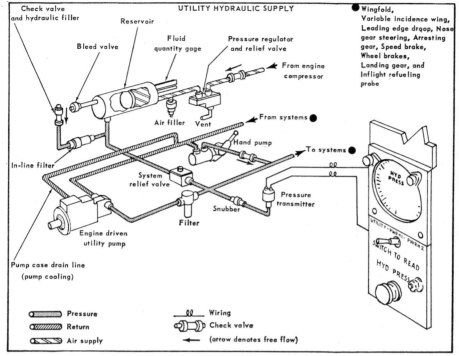

Courtesy Chance Vaught Aircraft, Inc.

3. A pictorial schematic is often easier to visualize.

lines. The ends of this pipe are tapered and held together with several bolts. See Illustration 4.

Seamless brass and copper pipe is manufactured in two standard weights —regular and extra strong; and in sizes ranging from 1/8″ to 12″ in diameter. Size is indicated by both the inside and outside diameters. The outside diameters are always the same as the corresponding nominal sizes of steel pipe. Both brass and copper pipe

4. Here are some ways that cast iron pipes are joined in piping installation.

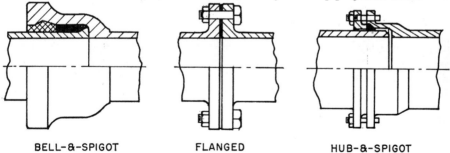

BELL-&-SPIGOT FLANGED HUB-&-SPIGOT

Preparing Piping, Heating, and Electrical Drawings **199**

are used for inside water service, fuel and oil lines.

Lead pipe and lead lined pipe is employed for conveying chemicals or where a piping system is subject to acid conditions. Sizes of these pipes are designated by the inside and outside diameters.

Galvanized iron pipe is chiefly for drinking water systems and is available in several different diameters.

Copper tubing is suitable for such work as hot and cold water lines, and for radiant heating systems. It is available in the hard and soft temper. Soft tubing is particularly adaptable for lines where considerable bending is required during installation. Hard temper tubing comes in straight lengths while soft tubing is in the form of coils.

Plumbing System

The water distribution piping for interior installations is chiefly of galvanized steel, copper or brass pipe. The waste system which includes all piping from sinks, showers, baths, and toilets, carries liquids and sewage to the outside of the building. These pipes are usually of cast iron and connect directly into the house sewer. The house sewer is the piping system beginning outside of the foundation and terminating at a street sewer branch or a septic tank. House sewer pipes are made of vitrified clay or cast iron.

The house drainage system includes such parts as traps, back-flow valves, vent stacks, and cleanouts. See Illustration 5. Vent stacks are vertical cast iron pipes which permit a continuous flow of air from the roof to the house drain. This free circulation of air retards the growth of harmful bacteria in the drain system, and eliminates poisonous gases and disagreeable odors. A cleanout consists of a branch pipe inside the basement wall to permit cleaning the house sewer. A house trap is located just beyond the sewer cleanout and provides a water seal that prevents odors from escaping back through the house fixtures. Back-flow valves are often installed in the system to stop any liquid from flowing back

5. These are the main units in a house sewage system.

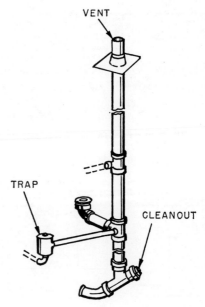

VENT

TRAP

CLEANOUT

from the street sewer into the house drainage system.

Pipe Fittings

Fittings are designed to make connections in piping systems and to change the direction of flow. They are made of cast iron, malleable iron, steel, brass, copper and other special metals. Pipe fittings fall into four general groups—screwed, flanged, welded and soldered.

Screwed fittings are found primarily in small piping systems, such as house plumbing, oil lines and hydraulic lines. Soldered fittings are used mostly on copper and brass piping and tubing where connections must be permanently and tightly sealed, especially in refrigeration units, radiant heating systems and other low pressure fluid lines. Flanged and welded fittings are employed in large piping systems where connections have to be strong enough to carry the weight of pipes and withstand high pressures.

Some of the more common pipe fittings are shown in Illustration 6. In-

6. These pipe fittings are used to connect various units in piping systems, or to change the direction of flow.

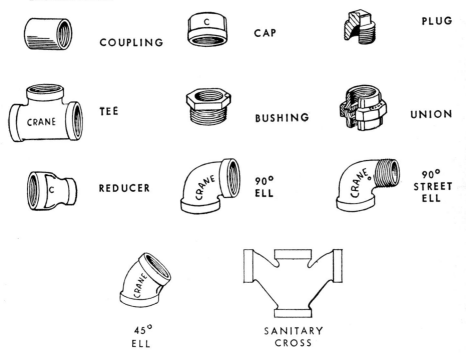

COUPLING CAP PLUG

TEE BUSHING UNION

REDUCER 90° ELL 90° STREET ELL

45° ELL SANITARY CROSS

cluded are the following:

Coupling—for connecting straight sections of pipe.

Cap—fits on the end of pipe to close it.

Plug—used to close an opening in a fitting.

Nipple—short piece of pipe for making connections to fittings.

Bushing—reduces the size of an opening in a fitting.

Union—used to close a piping system and to connect pipes that must be disconnected occasionally for repairs.

Tees, Crosses, Laterals—form the connections for lines branching off the piping system.

Ells—used to change the direction of pipe lines.

Reducer—permits the use of different pipe sizes in a piping system.

Pipe fittings are specified according to the nominal pipe size, material and strength factors or the pressure rating required.

Valves

The function of a valve is to control the quantity or the direction of flow in a piping system. Valves on small pipes are usually made of brass or bronze. Large piping systems are equipped with either cast iron or cast alloy steel valves.

The gate valve is probably the most frequently used valve for water and oil lines. The globe valve is especially adaptable for steam pipes. The needle valve is found in small systems where close control of flow is necessary. The diaphragm valve is designed for piping systems conveying acids, alkalies, and volatile substances. See Illustration 7.

Piping and Plumbing Symbols

In preparing a piping drawing or sketch, standard fittings, fixtures, valves and other units are usually shown by graphic symbols. Illustration 8 shows the basic symbols for piping and plumbing fixtures and fittings. The use of these symbols saves a great deal of time when a piping drawing is prepared.

Piping Drawing

The function of a piping drawing is to show the location of a piping system. The drawing may be a freehand sketch or a finished mechanical drawing. Quite often the preliminary layout is in the form of a sketch and later is made into a finished drawing.

The actual views of a piping system may consist of a single orthographic projection view, or a pictorial representation such as isometric or oblique. Occasionally a two or three view orthographic projection is prepared especially for systems which are basic in design and are installed frequently. See Illustration 9.

The presentation of a piping layout in either orthographic or pictorial projection is accomplished by what is known as single or double line representation. The single line drawing is more commonly used when installation of small pipe is involved or when making preliminary layouts and calculations. In a single line drawing single

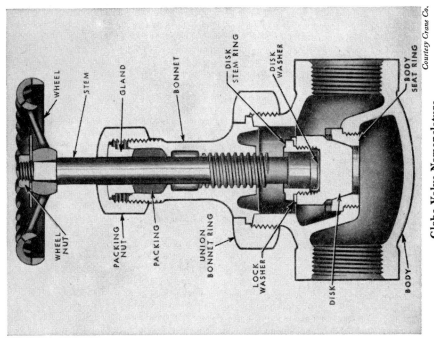

WHEEL

STEM

GLAND

BONNET

DISK STEM RING

DISK WASHER

BODY SEAT RING

WHEEL NUT

PACKING NUT

PACKING

UNION BONNET RING

LOCK WASHER

DISK

BODY

Globe Valve Nomenclature

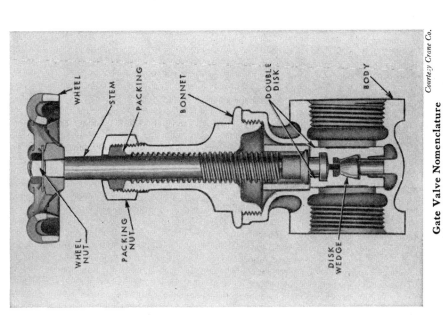

WHEEL

STEM

PACKING

BONNET

DOUBLE DISK

BODY

WHEEL NUT

PACKING NUT

DISK WEDGE

Gate Valve Nomenclature

7.   Valves control the quantity and flow of liquids in a piping system.

Preparing Piping, Heating, and Electrical Drawings   **203**

8. These are the graphical symbols used for pipe fittings and valves.

	FLANGED	SCREWED	BELL AND SPIGOT	WELDED	SOLDERED
BUSHING					
CAP					
CROSS REDUCING					
STRAIGHT SIZE					
CROSSOVER					
ELBOW 45-DEGREE					
90-DEGREE					
TURNED DOWN					
TURNED UP					
DOUBLE BRANCH					
LONG RADIUS					
REDUCING					
SIDE OUTLET (OUTLET DOWN)					
SIDE OUTLET (OUTLET UP)					
JOINT CONNECTING PIPE					
EXPANSION					
LATERAL					
REDUCING FLANGE					
REDUCER CONCENTRIC					
ECCENTRIC					
SLEEVE					

[1] *Abstracted from ASA Z32.2.3—1949,* with the permission of the publisher, The American Society of Mechanical Engineers, 29 West 39 Street, New York 18, N.Y.

	FLANGED	SCREWED	BELL AND SPIGOT	WELDED	SOLDERED
TEE					
STRAIGHT SIZE					
OUTLET UP					
OUTLET DOWN					
REDUCING	6 4	6 4	6 4	6 4	6 4
SIDE OUTLET (OUTLET DOWN)					
SIDE OUTLET (OUTLET UP)					
UNION					
ANGLE VALVE					
CHECK					
GATE (ELEVATION)					
GATE (PLAN)					
GLOBE (ELEVATION)					
GLOBE (PLAN)					
CHECK VALVE ANGLE CHECK	⟵——— SAME AS ANGLE VALVE (CHECK) ———⟶				
STRAIGHT WAY					
DIAPHRAGM VALVE					
GATE VALVE					
GLOBE VALVE					
SAFETY VALVE					

[1] *Abstracted from ASA Z32.2.3—1949*, with the permission of the publisher, The American Society of Mechanical Engineers, 29 West 39 Street, New York 18, N.Y.

9. Two-view pipe layout.

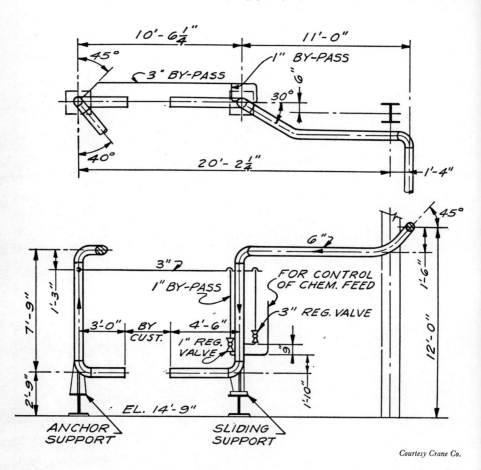

This is a typical piping installation drawing. Notice that both double-line and single-line representation are used to show the pipe sections. The existing steelwork of the building is shown to enable the contractor to assemble the pipe and fittings in the proper location with reference to equipment, machinery, etc.

10. Single line piping drawing.

lines are employed to designate pipe regardless of the pipe size. Conventional symbols are included for all fittings, valves and fixtures. See Illustration 10.

The double line drawing is more often prepared by manufacturers of piping equipment when a drawing is to be used repeatedly in similar installations. A double line drawing is also quite common for large piping systems. See Illustration 11.

The pictorial drawing of a piping system has a very decided advantage in that it can reveal changes in direction and differences in installation levels. See Illustration 12.

A house plumbing layout is begun by fastening a sheet of tracing paper over the floor plan and tracing the exterior walls and partitions. The layout is kept as simple as possible with only the wall thickness and openings for doors and windows shown. The main purpose of this layout is to show the location of the piping and fixtures in relation to walls and partition lines.

Dimensioning a Piping Drawing

Generally speaking, the same rules of dimensioning that govern orthographic and pictorial drawings also apply to pipe drawings. In each instance sufficient information must be provided so that the pipe fitter or plumber can accurately proceed without too much guesswork.

The following rules are particularly important in dimensioning a piping drawing:

1. All straight lengths of pipe should be dimensioned.

2. Location dimensions must be clearly indicated.

3. Pipe fittings, valves and other units are located by center-to-center distances.

4. Wherever possible, dimensions

11. Double line piping drawing.

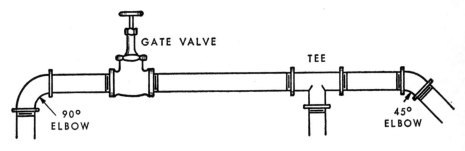

GATE VALVE

TEE

90°
ELBOW

45°
ELBOW

Preparing Piping, Heating, and Electrical Drawings **207**

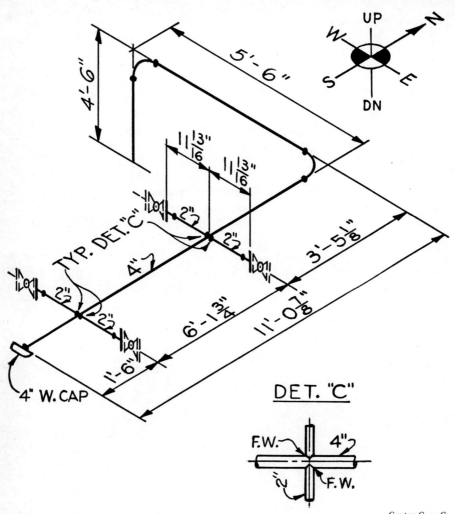

Courtesy Crane Co.

By using a single-line isometric drawing and standard symbols for fittings, valves, etc., the makeup of a pipe installation is easily understood by the erection crew as well as conserving much drafting time. Details are sometimes added using double-line representation to assist in interpreting construction of joints, etc.

12. Pictorial piping drawing.

should be placed on a solid dimension line instead of in between breaks of lines.

5. Size and kinds of pipe, fittings, valves and fixtures are identified at their location position or in a bill of material.

A heating system is intended to transmit heat from a point of generation to the place of use. A draftsman's job is not to design the heating system but to prepare the plan of the heating system from notes and sketches supplied by the heating designer. To effectively execute a heating drawing, a draftsman should have some knowledge of the fundamentals of heating and in addition be familiar with heating graphic representations.

Heating Systems

Heating systems are classified according to the medium used to convey the heat. The most common heating mediums are hot water, warm air, and steam. In the hot water and steam systems, the heat is transmitted through a series of pipes to panels or radiators. The horizontal pipes leaving the boiler are called *mains*. The vertical pipes are referred to as *risers*. Radiators are located directly beneath the windows. If they are placed along the inside wall, uncomfortable drafts result from the cooling effects of the windows.

In a warm air system, the heat is distributed through sheet metal ducts and is discharged into a room through registers or grills. Warm air is conveyed to the room either by gravity or a fan. The most common method is the forced circulation system, as it eliminates numerous large ducts radiating from the furnace. Horizontal ducts are called *leaders* and vertical

ducts *stacks* or risers. Ducts leading away from the leaders are known as *branches*. See Illustration 13. The fur-

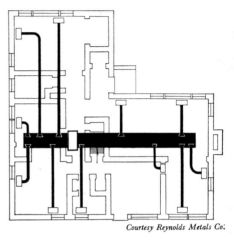

Courtesy Reynolds Metals Co.

13. Here is a simple warm air duct system.

nace for a gravity system is usually located in a central position to eliminate long leaders. Long leaders restrict the flow of air and cause considerable heat loss. With forced air, the location of the furnace is not as critical since the fan speeds up the flow of air and thereby reduces the heat loss. Cold air registers are placed in each room so that after the air has lost its heat, the cool air is returned to the heating plant.

Heating Drawings

The main purpose of a heating drawing is to show the location of the units involved in the heating system. The specifications of the various units along with a rough layout sketch are prepared by the heating engineer or contractor. The finished drawing may be either single view orthographic or a pictorial drawing, depending on the function of the drawing. As in plumbing drawings, work involving installation is shown by single or double lines with heating symbols serving to identify the units. See Illustration 14. Pictorial drawings are used largely to show some special units of a heating system or some particular method of installation.

Steam and hot water pipes are drawn in the same manner as described in the section on plumbing. Warm-air supply ducts are represented by solid lines. Duct sizes are given by showing first the horizontal dimension and second the depth dimension. However, the actual depth of the duct is not shown. Cold air ducts are drawn with dashed lines. Registers are located and scaled in the drawing to the given size.

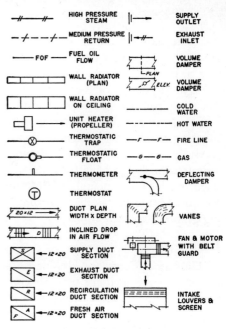

14. These symbols are used in preparing a heating drawing.

ELECTRICAL DRAWING

Schematic diagrams are used almost exclusively in laying out electrical circuits whether they are intended for ordinary house wiring, machine or appliance hook-up, radio or television construction. In each instance various graphical symbols are employed to represent the circuits, connections and equipment. The actual design of any electrical circuit is done by an electrical engineer. The draftsman's responsibility is to prepare a finished drawing from the engineer's notes and sketches. This assumes of course, that the draftsman possesses a general knowledge of electricity.

Standard Electrical Terms (See Illustration 15)

One of the most common types of electrical drawings prepared by draftsmen is a house wiring layout. A

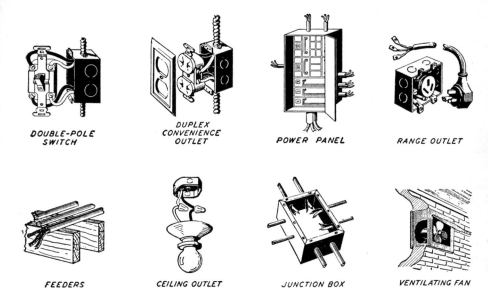

DOUBLE-POLE SWITCH DUPLEX CONVENIENCE OUTLET POWER PANEL RANGE OUTLET

FEEDERS CEILING OUTLET JUNCTION BOX VENTILATING FAN

15. These are some of the basic components of a house wiring system.

few basic electrical terms are included here for the benefit of the beginning draftsman.

Building Service: Conductors that supply electricity to a building from an outside distribution system are known as building services. The point at which the wires enter the building is called the service entrance.

Main Switches: The service entrance inside a building is connected to the service switch or main breaker switch which connects and disconnects the electrical power supply to the interior wiring system. From the main switch the power is carried to a panel box.

Panel Box: The panel box houses the safety components of a wiring system in the form of circuit breakers or fuses. A circuit breaker is a protective switch designed to open a circuit when there is an overload or a short circuit in the system. A circuit breaker eliminates the need for fuses and operates automatically.

Fuses are often used in place of circuit breakers. A fuse consists of a small piece of soft metal enclosed in a case or tube that melts and breaks the circuit in event of an overload. Both circuit breakers and fuses are intended to protect the wiring, lights and appliances in the building when trouble occurs in the circuit. Panel boxes are usually wired to include several circuits.

Conductor: A conductor is any copper or aluminum wire, bar or ribbon through which electricity flows. Conductor size in a circuit is governed by the amount of electricity it must carry. The more common types of conductors for ordinary house wiring are known as non-metallic sheathed cable, flexible armored cable and conduit. Non-metallic sheathed cable has two or more insulated copper wires covered with a tough braided outer jacket. It is the type most often used for indoor house wiring. Flexible armored cable has two or more insulated wires encased in a heavy galvanized steel protective cover. It is employed for exposed runs on walls or ceiling surfaces or concealed runs in hollow spaces of walls, floors and ceiling. This cable cannot be used for out-of-door purposes or in damp locations. Special cable must be utilized for out-of-door wiring such as plastic sheathed cable. Conduit, either of the thin-wall or rigid type, may be used for indoor and outdoor wiring. A conduit is steel tubing through which two or more insulated wires are drawn.

Circuits: In its simplest form, a circuit consists of the source of power, the devices which consume the electrical power and the conductor carrying the current from the source to the load and from the load back to the original source. Buildings today are wired to have several circuits insuring sufficient power to operate all of the customary devices found in a building. Thus there may be one or more circuits for the lights, a special circuit for the electric range, another for the clothes washer, one for the furnace and several more for various other purposes.

The three basic electrical circuits are series circuits, parallel circuits and series-parallel circuits. In a series circuit, the conductor runs from the source through two or more devices or loads and back to the source with only one path for the current. See Illustration 16. All the devices in this

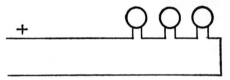

16. Notice how this series circuit is hooked up.

circuit must carry the same current. If one device fails to operate, the current ceases to flow and all the other loads stop functioning. A good example of a series circuit is the wiring of early style Christmas tree lights. When one light burns out, all the others go out. This circuit is not used for house wiring.

The parallel circuit is the one employed in house wiring. With this circuit the amount of current need not be the same for all loads. Moreover the operation of one device does not depend on the current passing through another since the circuit provides for the current to flow through more than one path. See Illustration 17.

17. The parallel circuit is the most commonly used circuit for house wiring.

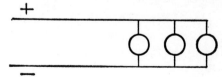

The combination series and parallel circuit provides for both series and parallel connections.

Volt: A volt is the unit used in measuring electrical pressure.

Amperes: An ampere is the unit that measures the electrical rate of flow (just as gallons per minute is used in a water system).

Watt: The watt measures the rate at which electrical energy is being used. Thus when one volt causes one ampere of current to flow, one watt of power is being used. One watt consumed for one hour equals one watt hour and 1000 watt hours equal one kilowatt hour which is the unit by which electricity is metered.

Switch: A switch is the device incorporated in a circuit to break the flow of current. A three-way switch when used in pairs can control the same light from different points. See Illustration 18.

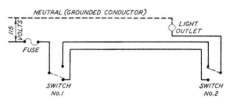

18. A schematic drawing of a three-way lighting circuit.

19. These are the basic electrical symbols used in architectural plans.

Courtesy American Standards Association

Ceiling	Wall	GENERAL OUTLETS
O	–O	Outlet.
Ⓑ	–Ⓑ	Blanked Outlet.
Ⓓ		Drop Cord.
Ⓔ	–Ⓔ	Electrical Outlet; for use only when circle used alone might be confused with columns, plumbing symbols, etc
Ⓕ	–Ⓕ	Fan Outlet.
Ⓙ	–Ⓙ	Junction Box.
Ⓛ	–Ⓛ	Lamp Holder.
Ⓛ$_{PS}$	–Ⓛ$_{PS}$	Lamp Holder with Pull Switch.
Ⓢ	–Ⓢ	Pull Switch.
Ⓥ	–Ⓥ	Outlet for Vapor Discharge Lamp.
Ⓧ	–Ⓧ	Exit Light Outlet.
Ⓒ	–Ⓒ	Clock Outlet. (Specify Voltage.)

CONVENIENCE OUTLETS

Duplex Convenience Outlet.
Convenience Outlet other than Duplex. 1=Single, 3=Triplex, etc.
Weatherproof Convenience Outlet.
Range Outlet.
Switch and Convenience Outlet.
Radio and Convenience Outlet.
Special Purpose Outlet. (Des. in Spec.)
Floor Outlet.

SWITCH OUTLETS

S   Single Pole Switch.
S$_2$ Double Pole Switch.
S$_3$ Three-Way Switch.

PANELS, CIRCUITS, AND MISCELLANEOUS

Lighting Panel.
Power Panel.
—— Branch Circuit; Concealed in Ceiling or Wall.
– – – Branch Circuit; Concealed in Floor.
----- Branch Circuit; Exposed.
Home Run to Panel Board. Indicate number of Circuits by number of arrows.
Note: Any circuit without further designation indicates a two-wire circuit. For a greater number of wires indicate as follows ⫫ (3 wires) ⫫⫫ (4 wires), etc.
Feeders. Note: Use heavy lines and designate by number corresponding to listing in Feeder Schedule.
Underfloor Duct and Junction Box. Triple System. For double or single systems, eliminate 1 or 2 lines. This symbol equally adaptable to auxiliary system layouts.
Ⓖ Generator.
Ⓜ Motor.
Ⓘ Instrument.
Ⓣ Power Transformer. (Or draw to scale.)
Controller.
Isolating Switch.

AUXILIARY SYSTEMS

Push Button.
Buzzer.
Bell.
Annunciator.
Outside Telephone.
Interconnecting Telephone.

Outlet Boxes: Conductors in a wiring circuit are terminated in one of several types of steel outlet boxes which then serve as receptacles for light fixtures or appliances.

Hot Wire: These are the black or red wires which carry the power as distinguished from the neutral wires which are usually white.

Grounding: Grounding is the connection of the electrical system to the ground so as to prevent damage from lightning and reduce the danger of shocks.

Wiring Symbols: Some of the basic house wiring symbols are shown in Illustration 19. These symbols are generally used whenever a wiring layout is prepared. There are no fixed rules governing the sizes these symbols must be drawn. The draftsman must exercise good judgment in laying them out so that their representation is in keeping with the conditions being described.

Schematic House Wiring Diagram

The first step in the preparation of such a drawing is to trace the floor plan of the area to be wired. Only wall thickness, window and door openings need to be included. Equipment and fixtures are next located in their proper position. Appropriate lines with the necessary symbols are then run to these points. No dimensions, as a rule, are included in this kind of drawing. See Illustration 20.

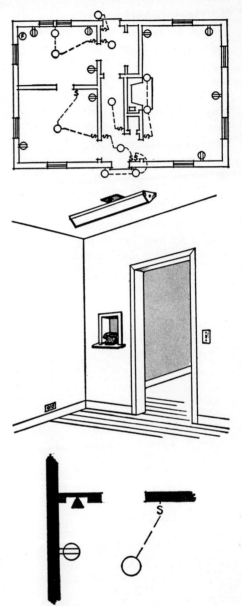

20. Typical wiring drawings for a room and home look like this.

Pictorial Electrical Drawings

Isometric or oblique drawings are often used to show specific electrical devices or installations, as well as to illustrate electrical units in instruction manuals and catalogs. They are sometimes used to show the assembly or erection of complicated wiring systems, particularly when dimensions must be included for clarity and understanding. See Illustration 21.

Appliance Circuit Diagrams

Circuits for radios, television sets, machinery or household appliances such as electric ranges, refrigerators or clothes washers are prepared with single lines or in pictorial form. With all of these circuits, regular electrical symbols or special symbols that are representative of the field are used. See Illustration 22 for symbols used in

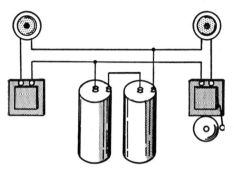

BELL & BUZZER SYSTEM

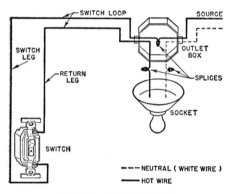

CEILING LIGHT SYSTEM

21. Pictorial drawings like those shown here are sometimes used to show specific installations.

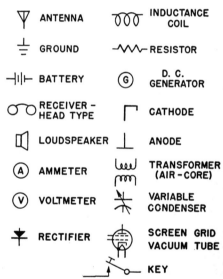

22. Special symbols are used to represent the units in radio circuits.

drawing radio circuits. Notice how these symbols are used in the radio circuit drawn in Illustration 23.

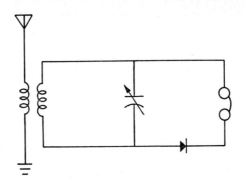

23. A schematic drawing of a crystal receiving set.

SELF QUIZ

1. What are the principal functions of schematic drawings?

2. How are the sizes of steel and iron pipe specified?

3. What is cast iron pipe primarily used for?

4. How is the size of copper pipe indicated?

5. What parts are generally included in a house drainage system?

6. What are the functions of vent stacks?

7. What are the four main classes of pipe fittings?

8. What are some of the more common types of valves and for what service are they used?

9. In a plumbing drawing, what is the difference between a single and double line representation?

10. How should a piping drawing be dimensioned?

11. What do these heating system terms refer to: mains, risers, stacks, leaders, branches?

12. What is the function of a cold air register?

13. What does a heating drawing show?

14. What are pictorial representations used in heating drawings?

15. Why are several circuits included in a house wiring system?

16. What is the difference between a circuit breaker and a fuse?

17. What governs the size of wires used in a circuit?

18. What makes up an electrical circuit?

19. How does a parallel circuit differ from a series circuit?

20. What should be included in a schematic electric wiring drawing?

PROBLEMS

1. Lay out a schematic diagram of the Door Chime or Buzzer system for your home.

2. Make an unscaled schematic layout in isometric of the piping system from the water heater to the kitchen sink of your home.

3. Make a drawing of the wiring diagram for a Telegraphic Code Practice Set using two dry cells, key, and buzzer. Use proper symbols.

4. Show by a diagram how you would operate a yard light from switches located in your garage and kitchen.

5. Make a freehand drawing of the floor plan of your Kitchen. On this drawing indicate the electrical outlets, switches, fan, etc., using standard symbols.

6. Prepare an electrical layout for the floor arrangement shown in Plan 24. Include the following:

LIVING ROOM	KITCHEN
Four outlets	One overhead light
BEDROOMS	Outlets for range,
One overhead light	exhaust fan,
Three outlets	refrigerator,
BATH	washer, dryer
One overhead light	HALL
One outlet	One overhead light
	One outlet

(Locate switches as needed)

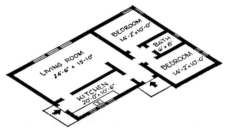

24. Floor Arrangement

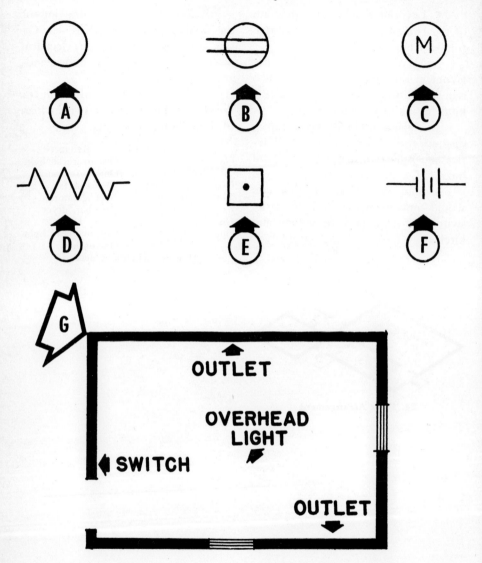

1. What do symbols A, B, C, D, E, and F represent?

2. Make a schematic sketch of the floor plan at G using symbols for all electrical units.

8
7
6
5
4
3
2
1
0

Drawing Graphs and Charts

UNIT 16

In the course of your work you may have to prepare reports requiring an explanation of factual data or statistical figures. The best way to present such information is by means of a graph or chart.

To appreciate the value of graphs and charts, you need only look through periodicals, textbooks, or newspapers. Time and again you will find that writers will resort to the use of a pictorial device when explaining something instead of trying to use written words. Most readers will understand the significance of a graph or chart, whereas they are likely to become confused or uninterested if the data is presented in tabular or written form.

As a draftsman you should not only know how to read graphs and charts but you should also be able to construct them. The material in this unit will describe some of the basic types of graphs and charts.

Types of Graphs and Charts

The terms graph and chart are often used synonymously, although some people do make a distinction between them. In general, a *graph* is said to be a pictorial presentation of numerical data for the purpose of showing comparisons, trends, or relationships. There are many different types of graphs. The most common are the *line graph*, the *bar graph*, and the *area graph*. To some extent, all of the others are variations of these three basic types.

A *chart* is frequently defined as a

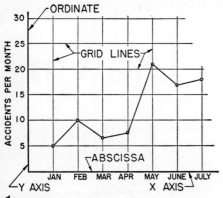

1. This is a typical simple line graph.

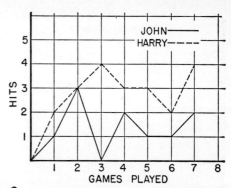

2. Here is how several sets of figures can be compared on one graph.

3. Here is another kind of line graph. Graphs make it easy to compare records with each other.

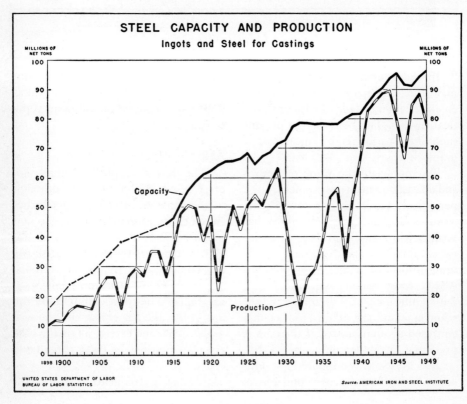

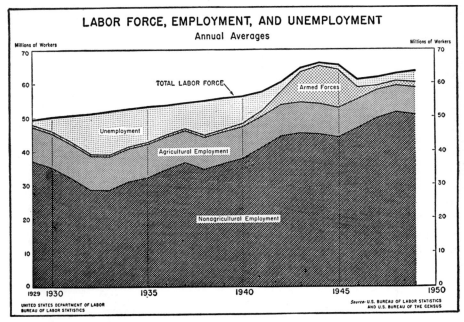

LABOR FORCE, EMPLOYMENT, AND UNEMPLOYMENT
Annual Averages

Millions of Workers

Millions of Workers

70

70

60

60

TOTAL LABOR FORCE

Armed Forces

50

50

Unemployment

40

40

Agricultural Employment

30

30

20

20

Nonagricultural Employment

10

10

0

0

1929 1930   1935   1940   1945   1950

UNITED STATES DEPARTMENT OF LABOR
BUREAU OF LABOR STATISTICS

Source: U.S. BUREAU OF LABOR STATISTICS
AND U.S. BUREAU OF THE CENSUS

4. Some line graphs are made like this. The graph should be arranged so that each item stands out clearly.

pictorial presentation of factual subject matter in outline form. Its purpose is to show such things as the ingredients of a product; the flow of material in a manufacturing process; the personnel organizations of an office, plant, or school; the historical events of a certain period; or the achievement record of students. Actually, any form that graphically illustrates subject matter can be considered a chart.

Line Graph

A line graph consists of a single line or a series of continuous lines plotted over a specific area. Suppose, for example, you had to show the school accident rate for a one-year period.

The simplest way to illustrate this would be by a line graph.

To construct a line graph, secure a sheet of cross-section or graph paper and on the left-hand side draw a vertical line. This line is known as the Y-axis or *ordinate*. On the bottom of the sheet draw a horizontal line, which is called the X-axis or *abscissa*. See Graph 1. Select some convenient area line on the vertical axis to represent the monthly accidents. Use similar area lines on the horizontal axis to represent the months of the year. Starting with the month of January, locate the accidents for that month and mark it with a point. Proceed in this manner for the remaining months. Then draw a solid line connecting each point.

Graph 2 shows you how to compare the number of hits you made in several ball games with those of some other player on the team. First plot your hits on the sheet. Then do the same for the hits made by the other player. Use a solid line to represent your hits and a dotted line for those of the other player. Notice how easy it is to compare the two records. Actually several sets of facts can be shown in this manner; however, each graph line must be made differently if the comparison is to stand out clearly. Very often the practice is to use different colored lines for each set of figures.

Bar Graph

A bar graph consists of a series of horizontal or vertical bars. The length of each bar represents the value or amount of a quantity being illustrated. For example, let us assume that you were asked to prepare a bar graph to show the relative standing of the teams in the American League. To construct such a graph, place a scale of values on the left side of the sheet as shown in Graph 5. On the bottom horizontal line lay off a bar for each team in the

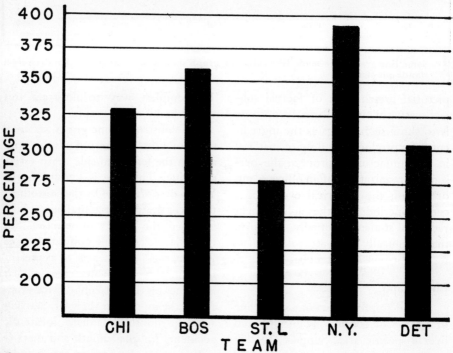

5. A typical bar graph showing the standing of baseball teams. Choose the kind of graph that best shows the data.

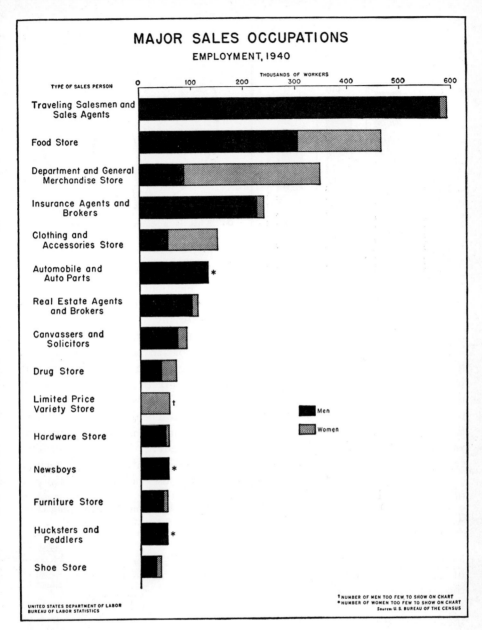

MAJOR SALES OCCUPATIONS

EMPLOYMENT, 1940

THOUSANDS OF WORKERS

TYPE OF SALES PERSON

Men
Women

UNITED STATES DEPARTMENT OF LABOR
BUREAU OF LABOR STATISTICS

† NUMBER OF MEN TOO FEW TO SHOW ON CHART
* NUMBER OF WOMEN TOO FEW TO SHOW ON CHART
Source: U. S. BUREAU OF THE CENSUS

6. Here is a bar graph with horizontal bars. Many items can be included in this kind of graph.

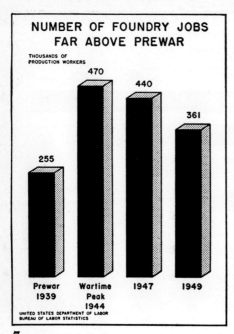

NUMBER OF FOUNDRY JOBS FAR ABOVE PREWAR

THOUSANDS OF PRODUCTION WORKERS

470   440   361   255

| Prewar 1939 | Wartime Peak 1944 | 1947 | 1949 |

UNITED STATES DEPARTMENT OF LABOR
BUREAU OF LABOR STATISTICS

7. This is another type of bar graph.

league. Space the bars evenly so they will be separated by at least one-half the width of the bars. Extend the bars to the values representing the respective teams and then place the exact values at the top of each bar. Shade each bar solidly or cross-hatch them.

Illustrations 6 and 7 show two other types of bar graphs.

Area Graph

An area graph is used to show amounts or percentage breakdown of some particular quantity. Although the area graph may assume many different shapes, the most common one is the circle or pie as shown in Graph 8. In this type, the circle is simply divided into a number of segments with each portion representing a value.

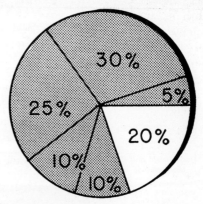

8. This is a common type of pie area graph.

Charts

As mentioned previously, a chart is used to illustrate factual subject matter pictorially. It may depict a manufacturing process, a personnel organization, or an achievement record. Since the nature of the information will vary greatly, no specific instructions can be given as to how such charts should be drawn. You will have to use your own ingenuity in presenting the material in the best possible manner. The only thing to keep in mind is to use the simplest form pos-

9. A school personnel organization chart.

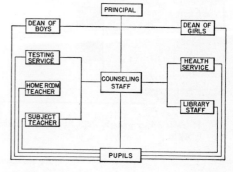

sible, because clearness of presentation is achieved more readily if the chart is easy to read. Very often, eye-catching symbols as well as the use of color serve to present the subject matter in a highly vivid manner.

Illustrations 9, 10, 11, 12, and 13 show a few typical charts.

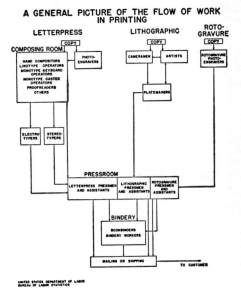

A GENERAL PICTURE OF THE FLOW OF WORK IN PRINTING

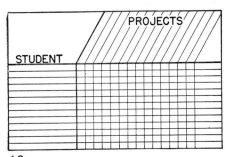

10. Student achievement record for use in a school shop.

12. Flow of work chart. Charts and graphs are used much in industry.

11. Manufacturing process chart. Complex operations are easily understood with the help of a chart like this.

THE STEELMAKING PROCESSES

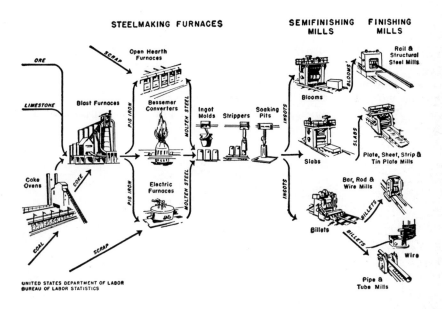

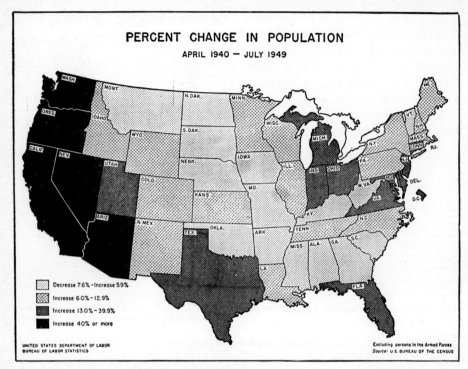

PERCENT CHANGE IN POPULATION
APRIL 1940 — JULY 1949

Decrease 7.6% - Increase 5.9%
Increase 6.0% - 12.9%
Increase 13.0% - 39.9%
Increase 40% or more

UNITED STATES DEPARTMENT OF LABOR
BUREAU OF LABOR STATISTICS

Excluding persons in the Armed Forces
Source: U.S. BUREAU OF THE CENSUS

13. A chart showing population change. Charts can be used to make it easier to understand anything about the world in which we live.

SELF QUIZ

1. Why are graphs and charts frequently used?

2. What is the difference between a chart and a graph?

3. What is the function of a line graph?

4. How many sets of values can be compared on a line graph?

5. How does a bar graph differ from a line graph?

6. In which direction should the bars of a bar graph be drawn?

7. For what purpose is an area graph used?

8. Charts may be developed for what different purposes?

PROBLEMS

1. Construct a line graph showing the following hourly temperatures. Use any desired size.

TEMPERATURE	HOUR
60°	7 A.M.
65°	8 A.M.
68°	9 A.M.
70°	10 A.M.
74°	11 A.M.
80°	12 M.
84°	1 P.M.
86°	2 P.M.
90°	3 P.M.
70°	4 P.M.
68°	5 P.M
60°	6 P.M.
55°	7 P.M.

2. Construct a horizontal bar graph using the following data:

SIZE OF COMMON NAILS	LENGTH OF NAIL
6d	2"
8d	2½"
9d	2¾"
10d	3"
12d	3¼"
16d	3½"
20d	4"
30d	4½"
40d	5"

3. Using the phases of construction listed below, prepare an operational chart showing the proper order involved in building a house. Design the chart to show the process simply and clearly.

BUILDING OPERATIONS

1. Plastering
2. Excavating
3. Electrical
4. Windows and doors
5. Foundation wall
6. Framing
7. Flooring
8. Laying out building
9. Heating installation
10. Plaster board
11. Brickwork
12. Insulation
13. Pouring footings
14. Painting
15. Fixtures
16. Cabinet work

4. Draw a chart showing the organization of your city government.

5. Prepare a line graph comparing the consumption of fuel oil for a two-year period.

MONTH	FIRST YEAR	SECOND YEAR
Sept.	150 gal.	140 gal.
Oct.	180 gal.	160 gal.
Nov.	186 gal.	200 gal.
Dec.	200 gal.	160 gal.
Jan.	220 gal.	260 gal.
Feb.	240 gal.	230 gal.
Mar.	180 gal.	190 gal.
Apr.	100 gal.	120 gal.
May	75 gal.	50 gal.

6. Assume that you played eighteen holes of golf. Construct a vertical bar graph using this data:

HOLE	STROKES	HOLE	STROKES
1	4	10	3
2	5	11	4
3	6	12	8
4	3	13	7
5	7	14	4
6	4	15	4
7	4	16	5
8	5	17	6
9	6	18	5

7. Draw a vertical or horizontal bar graph showing the cost of building a cabinet.

SUPPLIES	COST
Lumber	$8.50
Nails	.50
Screws	.75
Glue	.75
Fixtures	1.75
Filler	1.25
Stain	.35
Shellac	.35
Varnish	2.25
Sandpaper	.20

8. Prepare a pie graph showing the percentages of time spent in your various activities for a twenty-four-hour period.

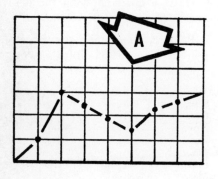

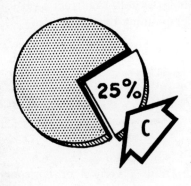

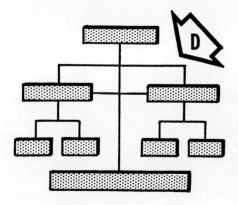

1. Identify the type of graphs shown in A, B, and C.

2. What would you call the illustration shown at D?

Making Prints and Reproductions

UNIT 17

Whenever it is necessary to have several copies of a drawing, the object is drawn on tracing paper or tracing cloth. This tracing is then used as a negative much as in the photographic process to produce the required number of prints.

There are many different methods for making prints. The most common prints are known as blueprints, Van Dyke prints, Ozalid prints, and black-and-white prints (B & W).

The History of Blueprints

There is very little written history on the subject of blueprinting, probably due to the fact that it was developed in part from other arts, notably photography. In some of its more recent ramifications it has returned to the once discarded printing process in a form of lithography but, during more than half a century, the true blueprinting operation has changed only in refinements of machinery and lighting.

It is said that a process similar to blueprinting was known to the Phoenicians in early biblical times. According to this record the Phoenicians made opaque drawings on translucent papyrus and used the sun to transfer these designs to their bodies.

The practical art of blueprinting is, however, a fairly recent discovery and its widespread use has only come about with the tremendous growth of industrial construction in the twentieth century.

All authorities seem to agree that

the discoverer of blueprinting was the famous English astronomer and scientist Sir John Frederick Herchel. In 1837 he observed that when light was impressed upon a paper coated with silver chloride it became tinted with nearly all the colors in the spectrum. Later he experimented with other chemicals and actually produced a blueprint design for the construction of his observatory telescope. He is said to have been the originator of the terms "positive" and "negative" in connection with solar printing, having used these terms for the first time in a report on his experiments to the Royal Society of England.

This process spread rapidly to France, Germany, and Switzerland, where many improvements in its practical application were developed. Its first introduction to the United States was in 1876, when the process was brought over and shown by the Swiss at the Philadelphia Centennial Exposition.

Originally, blueprinting was accomplished by solar light in much the same way that photographic prints are made by being exposed to light. In place of the photographic "negative," a drawing traced in opaque ink on translucent paper or cloth was used, and in place of the photographic "printing" paper a blueprinting paper was used. This blueprinting paper was a chemically treated or "sensitized" paper which, upon exposure to the sun through the translucent tracing cloth and a later washing, became a blue-print with the lines of the opaque drawing showing in white.

In an old book on formulas printed in 1884 appears this formula for coating or sensitizing paper for blueprinting:

CHEMICAL	PARTS BY WEIGHT
Prussiate of potash (red crystals)	1
Citrate of iron and ammonium	1
Water	10

With the exception that prussiate of potash is now known as potassium ferrocyanide and that direct current arc lighting, and more recently the mercury vapor tube, is used in place of the sun, blueprinting is fundamentally the same process that it was a half century ago. Of course, the machinery for blueprinting has been vastly improved over the makeshift devices of the bygone era but essentially the process has not been greatly improved.

Blueprints

A blueprint is a print having a blue background with white lines. This type of print is used extensively in the building and construction trades where prolonged outdoor use of the print is necessary. Blueprints are more permanent than other types insofar as fading is concerned, especially when they are exposed to direct sunlight for long periods of time.

Blueprints are produced by placing the tracing next to a piece of sensitized paper and exposing it to a source of light. This sensitized paper, called blueprint paper, has a pale yellowish-green surface which is coated with a solution of ammonia citrate of iron and ferrocyanide of potassium. When a light is transmitted through the tracing, a chemical action takes place wherever the light reaches the sensitized surface. By subjecting the exposed paper to a bath of clear water, the coating is washed away from the areas which are protected by the opaque lines on the tracing. This leaves a blue background with the image of the object in white lines. To secure an even greater contrast between the blue background and white lines, the print is often dipped in a solution of water and potassium bichromate and then thoroughly rinsed.

Blueprint paper is made with several degrees of sensitiveness, that is, some papers require longer periods of exposure than others. Whether a slow or fast paper is used depends entirely on the equipment available for exposure. A "slow" type paper must be exposed in a machine that produces a very intense light, whereas equipment having less intense light is required to expose a "fast" paper.

It is important to remember that when blueprint paper is not in use it must be kept in a tight metal container or stored in a darkroom. Otherwise, even ordinary light will destroy the effectiveness of the sensitive coating.

The actual production of a blueprint is done in some kind of a blueprint machine or in a sun frame. The sun frame is used only when an occa-

Courtesy The C. F. Pease Co.

1A. Sometimes this sun frame is used to make blueprints.

sional print is to be made, and no electrical equipment is available. It consists of a frame fitted with a glass front and a felt-lined backing plate. See Illustrations 1A and 1B. To make a print with this equipment:

1. Place the tracing in the frame with the lines in contact with the glass plate. Then lay the blueprint paper over it with the sensitized surface next to the tracing.

2. Lock the backing plate in position and expose the print to direct sunlight. The length of exposure will vary from one to several minutes, de-

1B. Making blueprints with a sun frame.

Courtesy The C. F. Pease Co.

pending on the intensity of the sun and the type of paper used. Usually it is a good idea to expose one or two small strips of blueprint paper first before making the final print. If the trial piece is a pale blue it is an indication that the exposure was not long enough. On the other hand, if the print has a very dark blue background, the print was overexposed.

3. Remove the print from the sun

2. The vertical blueprint machine uses electric light.

Courtesy The C. F. Pease Co.

frame and wash it in clear water. To bring out the contrast in the print, dip it in a potassium bichromate solution and then rinse it in water.

4. Hang up the print until it has dried.

Blueprint Machines

Whenever prints must be made in any quantity, a blueprint machine is used. There are two types of such machines: the vertical and the horizontal-continuous. The vertical machine consists of a cylindrical glass case with an electric arc lamp which descends at a uniform rate of speed down the center. See Photograph 2. The tracing and blueprint paper are held against the glass by a fabric curtain. The procedure for making a print is as follows:

1. Roll back the fabric curtain and place the tracing and blueprint paper against the cylindrical glass. Be sure the lines of the tracing are in contact with the glass and the sensitive coating of the blueprint paper is toward the tracing.

2. Close the curtain and set the timer for the correct period of exposure.

3. Turn on the switch to set the arc lamp in motion. When the lamp has completed its path of travel, turn off the switch and remove the paper.

4. Wash the paper in water and hang it up to dry.

If it is necessary to have typewritten matter on a print, the tracing should be typed with a piece of carbon paper behind it, with the carbon side toward the tracing. In this manner the typed information will show up much more clearly on the blueprint paper.

The horizontal-continuous blueprint machine is used when large numbers of prints must be made. This machine holds a roll of blueprint paper that unwinds as the tracings are fed into the machine. See Photograph 3. As the paper passes through the machine, it is exposed to a bank of lights. The print is then washed and dried. Some machines are even equipped with a washer and drier, making possible the production of prints in one operation.

Van Dyke Prints

Van Dyke prints are made in the same way as ordinary blueprints ex-

cept that Van Dyke printing paper is used instead of blueprint paper. Van Dyke paper is a thin semitransparent paper with a yellowish-green sensitized surface. When this paper is exposed and washed in water, the surface turns brown with white lines.

With Van Dyke paper it is possible to make what is known as a positive print, that is, a print having blue lines and a white background. To prepare such a print, the tracing is first placed so that the lines are against the sensitized coating of the Van Dyke paper. This paper is then exposed and washed. The next step is to use this negative print as the original tracing. The exposed side of the negative print is placed against the sensitized side of regular blueprint paper and exposed.

3. Continuous blueprint machine. With this machine, a large number of blueprints can be produced in a short time.

Courtesy The C. F. Pease Co.

The second exposure produces a positive print with blue lines and white background.

Ozalid Prints

Ozalid prints have either blue, black, or maroon lines on a white background. The color of the lines depends on the type of printing paper used. These prints are exposed in the same manner as ordinary blueprints. The principal difference is that after exposure Ozalid prints are not washed in water; instead they are developed in controlled dry ammonia vapor. Since Ozalid prints are developed dry, there is less distortion than on prints that are washed in water. They also have an added advantage in that notes or corrections can easily be made on the white background with an ordinary pencil.

When Ozalid prints first came into use, the developer consisted of a metal tube with a compartment in the base to hold the ammonia. See Photograph 4. The exposed print was inserted in the tube and the ammonia vapor allowed to circulate around the print for a sufficient period to develop it. Today a special combination printing and developing machine is available which quickly exposes and develops the print in a continuous process. See Photograph 5.

4. Ammonia tube for developing Ozalid prints.

Courtesy Eugene Dietzgen Co.

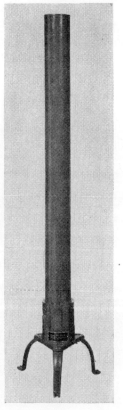

5. The Ozalid printing machine makes prints in a continuous process.

Courtesy Ozalid Division

Black-and-White Prints

The black-and-white print, commonly referred to as B & W, is a recent development and is rapidly growing in popularity. This print has black lines on a white background. The method used to produce a B & W print is much the same as the blue-line print of the Ozalid process, except that a special developing solution is used instead of ammonia. The production of black-and-white prints is called a "semimoist" process. The prints dry almost instantly, especially when the print machine is equipped with a heater roll.

Duplicating Tracings

Industries often wish to preserve their original tracings rather than to expose them to the hard use of continuous printing and filing. To make a duplicate tracing, an intermediate transparency is first made by exposing the original tracing on specially treated intermediate paper, cloth, or plastic film. The tracing in this instance is placed with the lines next to the sensitized side of the intermediate paper, cloth, or film. Prints are then made from this intermediate by placing the intermediate with the exposed side next to the sensitized side of the print paper.

SELF QUIZ

1. How can unexposed blueprint paper be identified?
2. What is the difference between slow and fast blueprint paper?
3. What determines whether a fast or slow blueprint paper is to be used?
4. Why must blueprint paper be kept stored in a dark room or metal container when it is not in use?
5. What is a sun frame?
6. To make a blueprint, how should the tracing be placed against the printing paper?
7. If after a blueprint is made and the background is pale blue, what may be the probable trouble?
8. What is the trouble if the background is very dark blue with indistinct lines?
9. After a blueprint has been exposed, why must it be washed in water?
10. How is a blueprint made in a vertical blueprint machine?
11. In what way does a continuous blueprint machine differ from a vertical machine?
12. How is it possible to secure clear typewritten matter on a blueprint?
13. What is a Van Dyke print?
14. How is a blue-line print made?
15. What are the outstanding advantages of Ozalid prints?
16. What is used to develop an Ozalid print?
17. What type of equipment is needed to expose and develop an Ozalid print?

18. What is meant by an intermediate?

19. What is a B & W print?

20. How do B & W prints differ from other types of prints?

PROBLEMS

1. Using an H or 2H pencil, make a pencil tracing of some drawing and prepare a print with whatever equipment is available in your drawing room.

2. Using a photographic negative, produce a blueprint. How does this print differ from an Ozalid, or B & W print of the same negative?

SUPPLEMENTARY PROBLEMS

The supplementary problems here included are to provide additional drawing experience for students who have shown greater drafting aptitude. Many of these are more complex than the regular text problems and consequently require more involved solutions. These problems should stimulate creative thinking and planning on the part of those students ready for more challenging work.

Unit 3

1. Construct an octagon within a 3¼" square as shown in Fig. 1. Measure the sides of the corner triangle and determine the difference in area between the octagon and the square.

2. Lay out the gage blank shown in Fig. 2.

3. Draw the three circles shown in Fig. 3 and determine the distance "X" using a decimal scale.

4. Draw the template shown in Fig. 4. Allow 9/16" material on all sides of the square and determine the diameter of the largest circular hole that can be cut out. What is the area of this opening?

5. Determine the total length of the crossed belt connecting the two pulleys shown in Fig. 5. In what direction will pulley "A" rotate?

6. Lay out gages A and B as shown in Fig. 6 to some convenient scale. Determine

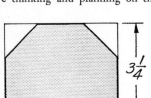

1. Octagon

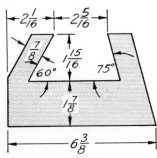

2. Gage Blank

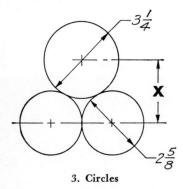

3. Circles

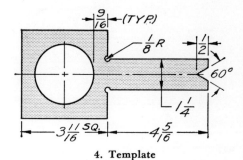

4. Template

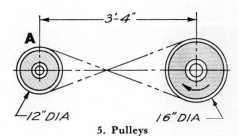

5. Pulleys

the area of each gage. Show by dotted lines how each gage is divided into sections to compute the area.

7. A—Construct a line tangent to two given circles.

B—Construct a regular pentagon in a 3¼″ Dia. Circle.

C—Construct a regular hexagon having a distance of 4″ across corners.

D—Construct an ellipse on the two axes shown.

8. Design a gasket to be used for the cover shown in Fig. 8. Maintain a minimum of ⅜″ material around all holes.

Unit 4

1. Prepare a full-size layout of the Brace sketched in Fig. 9 before bending. Determine the developed size of the piece.

2. Lay out the half-pattern of the Stencil Holder sketched in Fig. 10. Show full size.

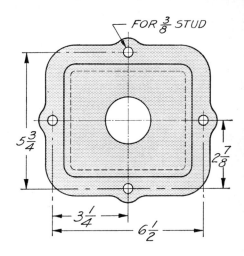

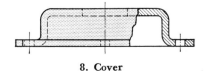

8. Cover

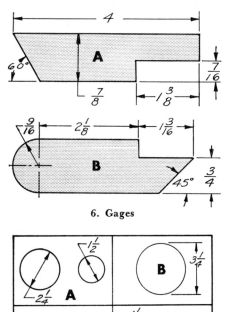

6. Gages

7. Geometric Construction

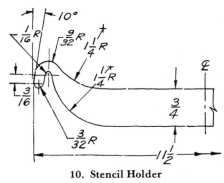

9. Formed Brace

10. Stencil Holder

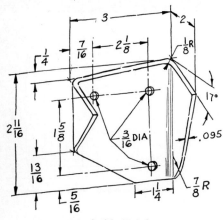

11. Guide Bracket

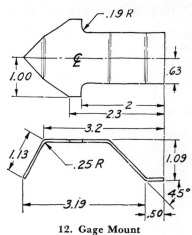

12. Gage Mount

3. Produce a flat layout of the Guide Bracket sketched in Fig. 11. Determine the overall sizes of the blank.

4. By means of a flat layout drawing, determine the amount of material needed to produce the Gage Mount shown in Fig. 12.

5. By means of layouts, determine how many pieces of the part sketched in Fig. 13 may be stamped out of a strip 1½" wide × 8'0" long. (Note, make a layout of a strip 1½" × 12": Allow 1/16" between pieces and at ends of strip.)

Unit 5

1. Divide an A-size sheet into four equal rectangular spaces and draw vertical and horizontal lines. Draw guide lines and letter ⅛" vertical capital letters, using lines of the complete alphabet and numerals. See Fig. 14.

2. Divide an A-size sheet into four equal rectangular spaces and draw vertical and horizontal lines. Draw guide lines and letter ⅛" inclined capital letters, using lines of the complete alphabet and numerals. See Fig. 15.

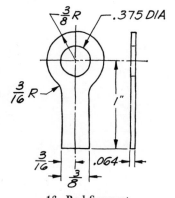

13. Rod Support

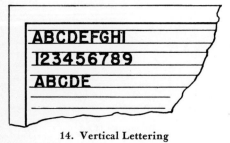

14. Vertical Lettering

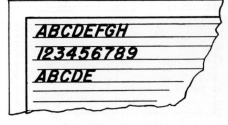

15. Inclined Lettering

3. Divide an A-size sheet into two equal areas by drawing a vertical centerline. Draw guide lines in ⅛″ capital letters, either vertical or inclined, composing an autobiography of yourself. Be careful to space words, sentences and paragraphs properly. Check your spelling and grammar.

Unit 6

1. Make a dimensioned layout drawing of the Drill Gage shown in Fig. 16. Use the following sizes:

A—2″   F—12°
B—135°   G—4″
C—½″   H—³⁄₁₆″
D—⁹⁄₁₆″   J—³⁄₈″
E—59°

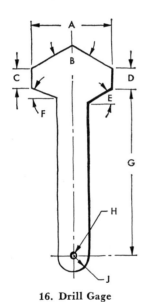

16. Drill Gage

2. Make a single-view dimensioned layout of the End Wrench shown in Fig. 17. Note that the open end is elliptical in shape. Use the following dimensions:

A—1½″   F—4¾″
B—¾″   G—⅛″
C—120°   H—⅜″
D—1¹⁄₁₆″   J—¹⁵⁄₃₂″
E—1³⁄₁₆″

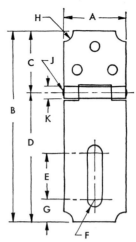

17. End Wrench

3. Make a two view dimensioned drawing of each part of the Hasp shown in Fig. 18. Locate three holes ¼″ Dia. as indicated. Material to be .060″ C. R. steel. Use the following dimensions:

A—1⁹⁄₁₆″   F—³⁄₁₆″
B—4⅝″   G—⁹⁄₁₆″
C—1½″   H—¼″
D—3⅛″   J—⅜″ Dia.
E—1⅛″   K—⁵⁄₁₆″

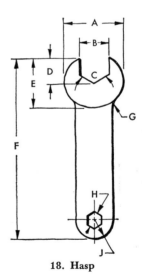

18. Hasp

4. Make a two-view dimensioned drawing of the Plumb Bob shown in Fig. 19. Use the following dimensions:

A—1″ Hex Bar   F—1¹¹⁄₁₆″
B—⅝″   G—¼″
C—¼″   H—³⁄₁₆″ Hole
D—⅜″   J—³⁄₁₆″
E—⅝″   K—8″ Taper
                                 per foot

5. Make a dimensioned layout drawing of the Wrench shown in Fig. 20 according to the following dimensions: Assume any size not indicated.

A—1¹⁄₁₆″   H—2³⁄₃₂″   P—⁷⁄₁₆″
B—2″   J—1¹⁄₁₆″   Q—1¾″
C—⅜″   K—1⅛″   R—2¹⁵⁄₁₆″
D—¾″   L—⅞″   S—¾″
E—7″   M—120°   T—⁹⁄₁₆″
F—⅝″   N—66°   U—1⁵⁄₁₆″
G—1¹³⁄₁₆″   O—⁹⁄₁₆″   V—1″
                                 W—10°
                                 X—1⁵⁄₁₆″
                                 Y—1⅜″
                                 Z—¼″

Unit 7

1. Construct the necessary views of the Pivot Mount shown in Fig. 21. Material—brass. Show all dimensions.
2. Make a 2-view drawing of the Punch shown in Fig. 22. Material—⁹⁄₁₆″ octagonal tool steel.

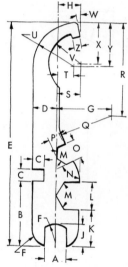

19. Plumb Bob

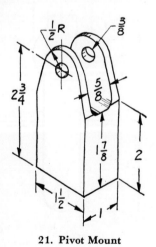

21. Pivot Mount

20. Wrench

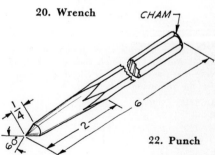

22. Punch

3. Make a completely dimensioned multi-view drawing of the Gage Stop, illustrated in Fig. 23. Material—steel, hardened.

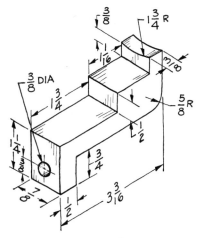

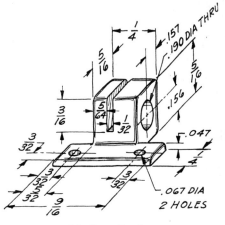

24. Gyro Bracket

4. Construct the proper views, completely dimensioned of the cast aluminum Gyro Bracket shown in Fig. 24.

23. Gage Stop

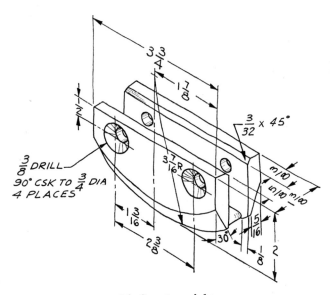

25. Counterweight

5. Prepare a dimensioned multi-view drawing of the Counterweight shown in Fig. 25. Material—aluminum.

Unit 8

1. Make a 2-view dimensioned drawing of the Hydraulic Pump Piston shown in Fig. 26. Include a ½ sectional side view. Material —brass.

2. Construct a top and a half-section side view of the spun steel missile Exit Cone illustrated in Fig. 27. Steel specification— SAE 1040. Include all dimensions.

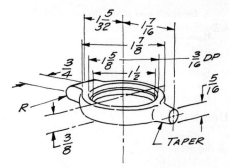

28. Thermocouple Clamp

3. Using Fig. 28, prepare a dimensioned 2-view drawing of the Thermocouple Clamp. Show one view in full section.

4. Draw the necessary views of the Punch shown in Fig. 29, designating the interior by means of a broken-out section. Material: Tool steel, hardened.

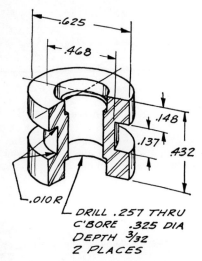

26. Hydraulic Pump Piston

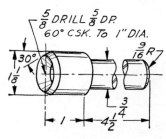

29. Punch

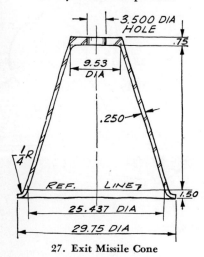

27. Exit Missile Cone

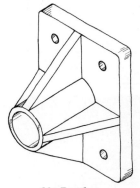

30. Bracket

5. Design a cast steel bracket as given in Fig. 30, using the following specifications:

Base—½″ × 6″ × 8″
Post—1¾″ I.D. × 2½″ O.D. × 4″
Ribs—⅜″ thick
Space 4 holes conveniently to accomodate ½″ bolts.
Fillets and rounds to suit.

Unit 9

1. Draw front, top and auxiliary views of the guide in Fig. 31.

2. Make a drawing of the Block shown in Fig. 32, incorporating your own measurements. Using the reference lines as indicated by the arrows, construct auxiliary views of the upper two inclined surfaces. A third auxiliary view may be drawn from the lower inclined surface.

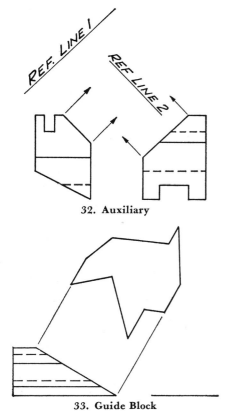

32. Auxiliary

31. Guide

3. Make a drawing similar to the one in Fig. 33, using any convenient measurements and scale. From the front and auxiliary view construct a right side view.

4. Draw the necessary views of the Bracket in Fig. 34. Show all dimensions.

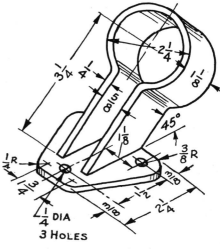

33. Guide Block

34. Bracket

Unit 10

1. Design a Ping Pong Net Bracket similar to the sketch in Fig. 35. Make complete dimensional detail drawings of each part, a welded assembly and final assembly drawing with parts list. Asssume any sizes not provided.

2. Using the partial detail drawings as shown in Fig. 36, make up a complete set of detail and assembly drawings of the Tool Post. Assume any sizes not given.

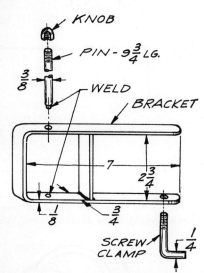

35. Ping Pong Net Bracket

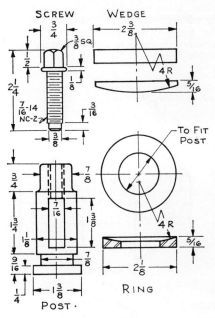

36. Tool Post

Unit 11

1. Lay out the pieces necessary to fabricate the duct work shown in Fig. 37.

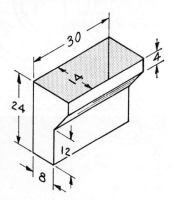

37. Duct

2. Develop the pattern for the Truncated Prism shown in Fig. 38.

3. Prepare a flat layout of the offset Transition Piece in Fig. 39.

Unit 12

1. From the isometric sketch of the Door Catch shown in Fig. 40, prepare a dimensioned cabinet drawing.

2. From the multi-view sketch of the Terminal shown in Fig. 41, make a dimensioned isometric drawing.

3. Prepare an angular perspective drawing of the house shown in Fig. 42.

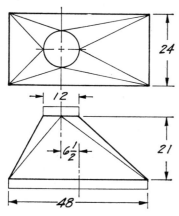

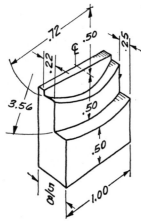

39. Transition Piece

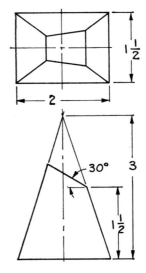

38. Truncated Prism

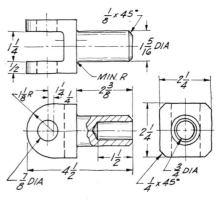

41. Terminal

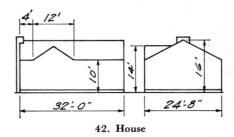

40. Door Catch

42. House

Unit 13

1. Make multi-view dimensioned sketches of each of the details of the Leveling Jack in Fig. 43 together with a pictorial assembly sketch.

Unit 14

1. Design a small Lake Cottage to be built on the plot shown in Fig. 44.
2. Using the outline and sizes shown in Fig. 45 plan the arrangements for a trailer to suit a family of 2 adults and 2 children under 14 years of age.

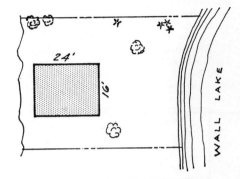

44. Lake Cottage Plot

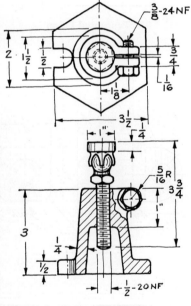

43. Leveling Jack

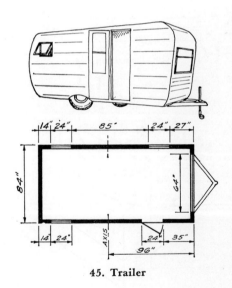

45. Trailer

Unit 15

1. Make a single line schematic diagram of the piping arrangement for an inverted open float steam trap, as shown in Fig. 46. Details for which there are no symbols available should be made in outline and noted.

2. Determine the total length of the pip-ing in a system containing the following:
    6—straight pipes—each 20 ft. long.
    4—90° bends having radius of 24".

3. Prepare a single line isometric draw-ing of the piping necessary to install a shower in your garage or basement. Tie into the present plumbing system as close to the water heater as possible.

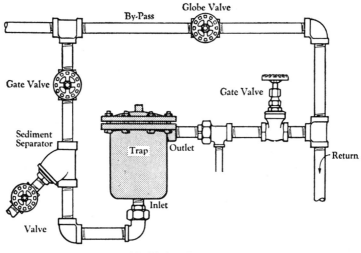

46. Piping Layout

DESIGN PROBLEMS

These problems are intended to help you apply your skills in preparing working drawings of products requiring some degree of original design. You may change the shape of the objects shown in any manner you wish. However, in each case you are to keep within the function and design specifications given for the problems. Include all required views and dimension completely.

A. Design a set of Salt and Pepper Shakers having plastic molded cases, brass caps and polyethylene plugs in bottom for refill as shown in A.

A. Salt and Pepper Shakers

B. Design a Table Lamp to accommodate a 16″ drum type shade similar to the one in Illustration B.

C. Design a Table Radio Case of molded plastic, having outside overall dimensions 6″ x 9½ x 4¾″.

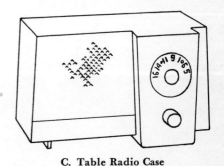

B. Table Lamp

C. Table Radio Case

D. Design a bathroom Towel Holder using either a round or square bar, as illustrated in D.

D. Towel Holder

E. Design a Carafe similar to the one shown in E, together with a metal stand. Prepare detail drawing of each of the component parts.

F. Design a 2-shelf Bookcase to be constructed of ¾″ walnut veneer panels. Legs are to be of solid walnut with brass ferrules. Overall size to be 32″ wide, 12″ deep and 30″ high. Recess ⅛″ hardboard panel for back. See Illustration F.

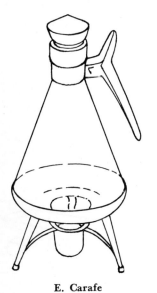

E. Carafe

F. Bookcase

Design Problems **251**

G. Prepare detail and assembly drawings of a Table Saw Stand to be fabricated from angle iron with legs 21″ long and a sheet steel top and shelf. Top of stand to be 16″ x 16″. Design the stand to be knock-down type, using machine bolts with nuts and lock washers for assembling. See Figure G.

G. Table Saw Stand

H. Design and prepare a detail drawing of a Mantel Clock, shown in Illustration H. Base suitable for mounting a 3½″ diameter clock mechanism. Material solid walnut. Overall size approximately 20″ x 3¾″ x 5½″.

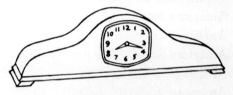

H. Mantel Clock

I. Make a layout drawing of an Aluminum Spice Rack capable of holding 8 shakers—1½″ diameter x 4⅜″ high. See Figure I.

I. Spice Rack

APPENDIX TABLES

Decimal Equivalents of Fractions	254
Thread Elements and Tap Drill Sizes, American National Coarse Thread Series	255
Thread Elements and Tap Drill Sizes, American National Fine Thread Series	256
American Standard Regular Square Bolts	257
American Standard Regular Hexagon Bolts	258
American Standard Regular Semi-finished Hexagon Bolts . . .	259
Milled Studs, American Standard Coarse Thread Series . . .	260
American Standard Regular Square Nuts	261
American Standard Regular Hexagon and Hexagon Jam Nuts . .	262
American Standard Hexagon Head Cap Screws	263
American Standard Flat Head Cap Screws	264
American Standard Fillister Head Cap Screws	265
American Standard Round Head Cap Screws	265
American Standard Hexagon Socket Head Cap Screws . . .	266
American Standard Flat Head Machine Screws	267
American Standard Round Head Machine Screws	268
American Standard Oval Head Machine Screws	269
American Standard Fillister Head Machine Screws . . .	270
American Standard Square Head Set Screws	271
American Standard Steel Wood Screws	272
Woodruff Keys	273

DECIMAL EQUIVALENTS OF FRACTIONS

Fraction	Decimal		Fraction	Decimal
1/64	0.015625		33/64	0.515625
1/32	0.03125		17/32	0.53125
3/64	0.046875		35/64	0.546875
1/16	0.0625		9/16	0.5625
5/64	0.078125		37/64	0.578125
3/32	0.09375		19/32	0.59375
7/64	0.109375		39/64	0.609375
1/8	0.125		5/8	0.625
9/64	0.140625		41/64	0.640625
5/32	0.15625		21/32	0.65625
11/64	0.171875		43/64	0.671875
3/16	0.1875		11/16	0.6875
13/64	0.203125		45/64	0.703125
7/32	0.21875		23/32	0.71875
15/64	0.234375		47/64	0.734375
1/4	0.250		3/4	0.750
17/64	0.265625		49/64	0.765625
9/32	0.28125		25/32	0.78125
19/64	0.296875		51/64	0.796875
5/16	0.3125		13/16	0.8125
21/64	0.328125		53/64	0.828125
11/32	0.34375		27/32	0.84375
23/64	0.359375		55/64	0.859375
3/8	0.375		7/8	0.875
25/64	0.390625		57/64	0.890625
13/32	0.40625		29/32	0.90625
27/64	0.421875		59/64	0.921875
7/16	0.4375		15/16	0.9375
29/64	0.453125		61/64	0.953125
15/32	0.46875		31/32	0.96875
31/64	0.484375		63/64	0.984375
1/2	0.500		1	1.

THREAD ELEMENTS AND TAP DRILL SIZES
AMERICAN NATIONAL COARSE THREAD SERIES

Sizes	Threads Per Inch	DIAMETERS (Basic)			TAP DRILLS	
		Major Diameter —Inches	Pitch Diameter —Inches	Minor Diameter —Inches	Tap Drill To Produce Approx. 75% Full Thread	Decimal Equivalent of Tap Drill —Inches
1	64	0.073	0.0629	0.0527	1.45 mm	.0571
2	56	.086	.0744	.0628	1.75 mm	.0689
3	48	.099	.0855	.0719	2.00 mm	.0787
4	40	.112	.0958	.0795	2.20 mm	.0866
5	40	.125	.1088	.0925	39	.0995
6	32	.138	.1177	.0974	36	.1065
8	32	.164	.1437	.1234	3.40 mm	.1339
10	24	.190	.1629	.1359	25	.1495
12	24	.216	.1889	.1619	4.40 mm	.1732
1/4	20	.2500	.2175	.1850	7	.2010
5/16	18	.3125	.2764	.2403	F	.2570
3/8	16	.3750	.3344	.2938	5/16	.3125
7/16	14	.4375	.3911	.3447	U	.3680
1/2	13	.5000	.4500	.4001	27/64	.4219
9/16	12	.5625	.5084	.4542	31/64	.4844
5/8	11	.6250	.5660	.5069	17/32	.5312
3/4	10	.7500	.6850	.6201	16.5 mm	.6496
7/8	9	.8750	.8028	.7307	49/64	.7656
1	8	1.0000	.9188	.8376	7/8	.8750
1 1/8	7	1.1250	1.0322	.9394	63/64	.9844
1 1/4	7	1.2500	1.1572	1.0644	1 7/64	1.1093
1 1/2	6	1.5000	1.3917	1.2835	34.0 mm	1.3386
1 3/4	5	1.7500	1.6201	1.4902	39.5 mm	1.5551
2	4 1/2	2.0000	1.8557	1.7113	1 25/32	1.7812
2 1/4	4 1/2	2.2500	2.1057	1.9613	2 1/32	2.0312
2 1/2	4	2.5000	2.3376	2.1752	2 1/4	2.2500
2 3/4	4	2.7500	2.5876	2.4252	2 1/2	2.5000
3	4	3.0000	2.8376	2.6752	70.0 mm	2.7559

THREAD ELEMENTS AND TAP DRILL SIZES
AMERICAN NATIONAL FINE THREAD SERIES

Sizes	Threads Per Inch	DIAMETERS (Basic)			TAP DRILLS	
		Major Diameter —Inches	Pitch Diameter —Inches	Minor Diameter —Inches	Tap Drill To Produce Approx. 75% Full Thread	Decimal Equivalent of Tap Drill —Inches
0	80	0.060	0.0519	0.0438	**1.20** mm	.0472
1	72	.073	.0640	.0550	**53**	.0595
2	64	.086	.0759	.0657	**1.80** mm	.0709
3	56	.099	.0874	.0758	**45**	.0820
4	48	.112	.0985	.0849	**2.30** mm	.0905
5	44	.125	.1102	.0955	**2.60** mm	.1024
6	40	.138	.1218	.1055	**33**	.1130
8	36	.164	.1460	.1279	**29**	.1360
10	32	.190	.1697	.1494	**21**	.1590
12	28	.216	.1928	.1696	**4.60** mm	.1811
1/4	28	.2500	.2268	.2036	**5.50** mm	.2165
5/16	24	.3125	.2854	.2584	**I**	.2720
3/8	24	.3750	.3479	.3209	**8.50** mm	.3346
7/16	20	.4375	.4050	.3725	**9.90** mm	.3898
1/2	20	.5000	.4675	.4350	**11.5** mm	.4527
9/16	18	.5625	.5264	.4903	**13.0** mm	.5118
5/8	18	.6250	.5889	.5528	**14.5** mm	.5709
3/4	16	.7500	.7094	.6688	**17.5** mm	.6890
7/8	14	.8750	.8286	.7822	**20.5** mm	.8071
1	14	1.0000	.9536	.9072	**59/64**	.9218
1 1/8	12	1.1250	1.0709	1.0167	**26.5** mm	1.0433
1 1/4	12	1.2500	1.1959	1.1417	**1 11/64**	1.1719
1 1/2	12	1.5000	1.4459	1.3917	**36.0** mm	1.4173
1 3/4	12	1.7500	1.6959	1.6417	**1 43/64**	1.6718
2	12	2.0000	1.9459	1.8917	**1 59/64**	1.9218
2 1/4	12	2.2500	2.1959	2.1417	**2 11/64**	2.1718
2 1/2	12	2.5000	2.4459	2.3917	**61.5** mm	2.4212
2 3/4	12	2.7500	2.6959	2.6417	**2 43/64**	2.6718
3	10	3.0000	2.9350	2.8701	**2 29/32**	2.9063

AMERICAN STANDARD
REGULAR SQUARE BOLTS[1]

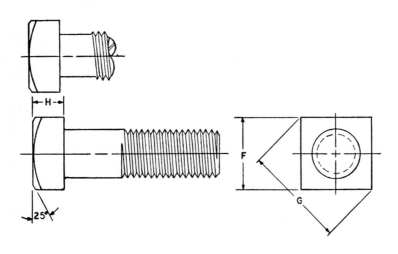

Nominal Size or Basic Major Diameter of Thread	Body Diam	Width Across Flats F	Width Across Corners G	Height H
$\frac{1}{4}$	.280	$\frac{3}{8}$	.530	$1\frac{1}{64}$
$\frac{5}{16}$	.342	$\frac{1}{2}$	.707	$1\frac{3}{64}$
$\frac{3}{8}$	.405	$\frac{9}{16}$	.795	$\frac{1}{4}$
$\frac{7}{16}$	.468	$\frac{5}{8}$	.884	$1\frac{9}{64}$
$\frac{1}{2}$	.530	$\frac{3}{4}$	1.061	$2\frac{1}{64}$
$\frac{5}{8}$	.675	$\frac{15}{16}$	1.326	$2\frac{7}{64}$
$\frac{3}{4}$	.800	$1\frac{1}{8}$	1.591	$\frac{1}{2}$
$\frac{7}{8}$	.938	$1\frac{5}{16}$	1.856	$1\frac{9}{32}$
1	1.063	$1\frac{1}{2}$	2.121	$2\frac{1}{32}$
$1\frac{1}{8}$	1.188	$1\frac{11}{16}$	2.386	$\frac{3}{4}$
$1\frac{1}{4}$	1.313	$1\frac{7}{8}$	2.652	$2\frac{7}{32}$
$1\frac{3}{8}$	1.469	$2\frac{1}{16}$	2.917	$2\frac{9}{32}$
$1\frac{1}{2}$	1.594	$2\frac{1}{4}$	3.182	1
$1\frac{5}{8}$	1.719	$2\frac{7}{16}$	3.447	$1\frac{3}{32}$

[1] *Abstracted from ASA B18.2—1952*

Minimum thread length shall be twice the diameter plus $\frac{1}{4}$ in. for lengths up to and including 6 and twice the diameter plus $\frac{1}{2}$ in. for lengths over 6.

Thread shall be coarse-thread series, class 2A.

AMERICAN STANDARD
REGULAR HEXAGON BOLTS[1]

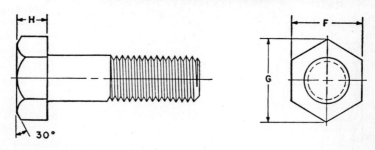

Nominal Size or Basic Major Diameter of Thread	Body Diam	Width Across Flats F	Width Across Corners G	Height H
$\frac{1}{4}$	.280	$\frac{7}{16}$	.505	$1\frac{1}{64}$
$\frac{5}{16}$	.342	$\frac{1}{2}$	.577	$\frac{7}{32}$
$\frac{3}{8}$	.405	$\frac{9}{16}$	.650	$\frac{1}{4}$
$\frac{7}{16}$	.468	$\frac{5}{8}$	.722	$1\frac{9}{64}$
$\frac{1}{2}$	.530	$\frac{3}{4}$	.866	$1\frac{1}{32}$
$\frac{5}{8}$	.675	$1\frac{5}{16}$	1.083	$2\frac{7}{64}$
$\frac{3}{4}$	.800	$1\frac{1}{8}$	1.299	$\frac{1}{2}$
$\frac{7}{8}$	.938	$1\frac{5}{16}$	1.516	$3\frac{7}{64}$
1	1.063	$1\frac{1}{2}$	1.732	$4\frac{3}{64}$
$1\frac{1}{8}$	1.188	$1\frac{11}{16}$	1.949	$\frac{3}{4}$
$1\frac{1}{4}$	1.313	$1\frac{7}{8}$	2.165	$2\frac{7}{32}$
$1\frac{3}{8}$	1.469	$2\frac{1}{16}$	2.382	$2\frac{9}{32}$
$1\frac{1}{2}$	1.594	$2\frac{1}{4}$	2.598	1
$1\frac{5}{8}$	1.719	$2\frac{7}{16}$	2.815	$1\frac{1}{16}$
$1\frac{3}{4}$	1.844	$2\frac{5}{8}$	3.031	$1\frac{5}{32}$
$1\frac{7}{8}$	1.969	$2\frac{13}{16}$	3.248	$1\frac{7}{32}$
2	2.094	3	3.464	$1\frac{11}{32}$
$2\frac{1}{4}$	2.375	$3\frac{3}{8}$	3.897	$1\frac{1}{2}$
$2\frac{1}{2}$	2.625	$3\frac{3}{4}$	4.330	$1\frac{21}{32}$
$2\frac{3}{4}$	2.875	$4\frac{1}{8}$	4.763	$1\frac{13}{16}$
3	3.125	$4\frac{1}{2}$	5.196	2
$3\frac{1}{4}$	3.438	$4\frac{7}{8}$	5.629	$2\frac{3}{16}$
$3\frac{1}{2}$	3.688	$5\frac{1}{4}$	6.062	$2\frac{5}{16}$
$3\frac{3}{4}$	3.938	$5\frac{5}{8}$	6.495	$2\frac{1}{2}$
4	4.188	6	6.928	$2\frac{11}{16}$

[1] *Abstracted from ASA B18.2—1952*
Minimum thread length shall be twice the diameter plus $\frac{1}{4}$ in. for lengths up to and including 6 in. and twice the diameter plus $\frac{1}{2}$ in. for lengths over 6 in.
Thread shall be coarse-thread series, class 2A.

AMERICAN STANDARD
REGULAR SEMI-FINISHED HEXAGON BOLTS[1]

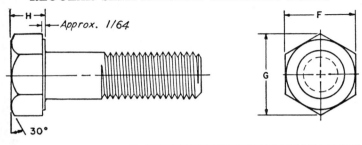

Nominal Size or Basic Major Diameter of Thread	Body Diam	Width Across Flats F	Width Across Corners G	Height H
1/4	.280	7/16	.505	5/32
5/16	.342	1/2	.577	13/64
3/8	.405	9/16	.650	15/64
7/16	.468	5/8	.722	9/32
1/2	.530	3/4	.866	5/16
5/8	.675	15/16	1.083	25/64
3/4	.800	1 1/8	1.299	15/32
7/8	.938	1 5/16	1.516	35/64
1	1.063	1 1/2	1.732	39/64
1 1/8	1.188	1 11/16	1.949	11/16
1 1/4	1.313	1 7/8	2.165	25/32
1 3/8	1.469	2 1/16	2.382	27/32
1 1/2	1.594	2 1/4	2.598	15/16
1 5/8	1.719	2 7/16	2.815	1
1 3/4	1.844	2 5/8	3.031	1 3/32
1 7/8	1.969	2 13/16	3.248	1 5/32
2	2.094	3	3.464	1 7/32
2 1/4	2.375	3 3/8	3.897	1 3/8
2 1/2	2.625	3 3/4	4.330	1 17/32
2 3/4	2.875	4 1/8	4.763	1 11/16
3	3.125	4 1/2	5.196	1 7/8
3 1/4	3.438	4 7/8	5.629	2
3 1/2	3.688	5 1/4	6.062	2 1/8
3 3/4	3.938	5 5/8	6.495	2 5/16
4	4.188	6	6.928	2 1/2

[1] *Abstracted from ASA B18.2—1952*

Minimum thread length shall be twice the diameter plus 1/4 in. for lengths up to and including 6 in.; twice the diameter plus 1/2 in. for lengths over 6 in. The tolerance shall be plus 3/16 in. or 2 1/2 threads, whichever is greater. On products that are too short for minimum thread lengths, the distance from the bearing surface of the head to the first complete thread shall not exceed the length of 2 1/2 threads, as measured with a ring thread gage, for sizes up to and including 1 in. and 3 1/2 threads for sizes larger than 1 in.

Thread shall be coarse-thread series, class 2A.

Point shall be flat and chamfered or rounded at manufacturer's option, length of point not to exceed length of 1 1/2 threads from extreme point to first full thread.

MILLED STUDS
AMERICAN STANDARD COARSE THREAD SERIES

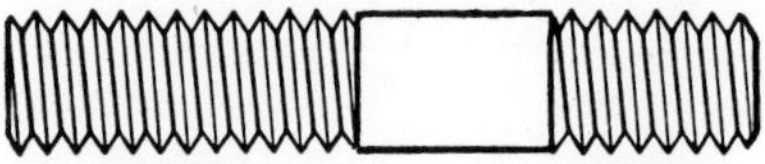

N = Nut End
T = Tap End

OVERALL LENGTH		DIAMETER 1/4-20	5/16-18	3/8-16	7/16-14	1/2-13	5/8-11	3/4-10	7/8-9	1-8
1 1/4″	N	5/8	5/8	5/8	5/8	5/8	5/8	...	...	...
	T	1/2	1/2	1/2	1/2	1/2	5/8	...	...	...
1 1/2″	N	5/8	5/8	5/8	3/4	3/4	3/4	...	...	...
	T	1/2	1/2	1/2	9/16	1/2	5/8	...	...	...
1 3/4″	N	5/8	5/8	5/8	3/4	3/4	7/8	7/8	...	...
	T	1/2	1/2	1/2	9/16	5/8	3/4	3/4	...	...
2″	N	3/4	3/4	3/4	3/4	3/4	7/8	7/8	...	...
	T	1/2	1/2	1/2	9/16	5/8	3/4	7/8	...	...
2 1/4″	N	...	3/4	3/4	3/4	3/4	7/8	7/8	1	...
	T	...	1/2	1/2	9/16	5/8	3/4	7/8	1	...
2 1/2″	N	...	3/4	3/4	3/4	3/4	7/8	7/8	1 1/8	1 1/4
	T	...	1/2	1/2	9/16	5/8	3/4	7/8	1	1 1/8
2 3/4″	N	...	...	3/4	3/4	7/8	1	1	1 1/8	1 1/4
	T	...	...	1/2	9/16	3/4	7/8	7/8	1	1 1/8
3″	N	...	...	3/4	7/8	7/8	1	1	1 1/8	1 1/4
	T	...	...	1/2	9/16	3/4	7/8	7/8	1	1 1/8
3 1/4″	N	...	...	...	7/8	1	1	1	1 1/8	1 1/4
	T	...	...	...	9/16	3/4	7/8	7/8	1	1 1/8
3 1/2″	N	...	...	...	7/8	1	1	1 1/4	1 1/4	1 1/4
	T	...	...	...	9/16	3/4	7/8	7/8	1	1 1/8
3 3/4″	N	...	...	...	1	1	1 1/4	1 1/4	1 1/4	1 1/4
	T	...	...	...	1 1/16	3/4	7/8	7/8	1	1 1/8
4″	N	...	...	...	1	1 1/4	1 1/4	1 1/4	1 1/4	1 1/2
	T	...	...	...	1 1/16	3/4	7/8	1	1	1 1/4
4 1/4″	N	...	...	...	...	1 1/4	1 1/4	1 1/2	1 1/2	1 1/2
	T	...	...	...	...	7/8	7/8	1	1 1/8	1 1/4
4 1/2″	N	...	...	...	...	1 1/4	1 1/4	1 1/2	1 1/2	1 3/4
	T	...	...	...	...	7/8	7/8	1	1 1/8	1 1/4
4 3/4″	N	...	...	...	...	1 1/4	1 1/4	1 1/2	1 1/2	1 3/4
	T	...	...	...	...	7/8	7/8	1	1 1/8	1 1/4
5″	N	...	...	...	...	1 1/4	1 1/2	1 1/2	1 3/4	2
	T	...	...	...	...	7/8	7/8	1	1 1/8	1 1/4
5 1/2″	N	...	...	...	...	...	1 1/2	1 3/4	1 3/4	2
	T	...	...	...	...	...	7/8	1	1 1/8	1 1/2
6″	N	...	...	...	...	...	1 1/2	1 3/4	1 3/4	2
	T	...	...	...	...	...	7/8	1	1 1/4	1 1/2

All dimensions expressed in inches.

AMERICAN STANDARD
REGULAR SQUARE NUTS[1]

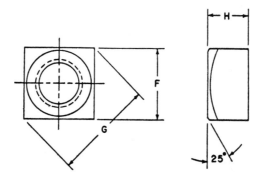

Nominal Size or Basic Major Diameter of Thread	Width Across Flats F	Width Across Corners G	Thickness H
1/4	7/16	.619	7/32
5/16	9/16	.795	17/64
3/8	5/8	.884	21/64
7/16	3/4	1.061	3/8
1/2	13/16	1.149	7/16
5/8	1	1.414	35/64
3/4	1 1/8	1.591	21/32
7/8	1 5/16	1.856	49/64
1	1 1/2	2.121	7/8
1 1/8	1 11/16	2.386	1
1 1/4	1 7/8	2.652	1 3/32
1 3/8	2 1/16	2.917	1 13/64
1 1/2	2 1/4	3.182	1 5/16
1 5/8	2 7/16	3.447	1 27/64

[1] Abstracted from ASA B18.2—1952

AMERICAN STANDARD
REGULAR HEXAGON AND HEXAGON JAM NUTS[1]

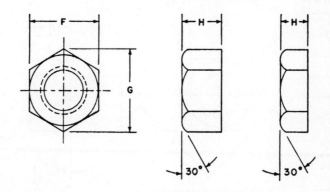

Nominal Size or Basic Major Diameter of Thread	Width Across Flats F	Width Across Corners G	Thickness Regular Nuts H	Thickness Regular Jam Nuts H
$\frac{1}{4}$	$\frac{7}{16}$	.505	$\frac{7}{32}$	$\frac{5}{32}$
$\frac{5}{16}$	$\frac{9}{16}$	.650	$\frac{17}{64}$	$\frac{3}{16}$
$\frac{3}{8}$	$\frac{5}{8}$	.722	$\frac{21}{64}$	$\frac{7}{32}$
$\frac{7}{16}$	$\frac{3}{4}$	.866	$\frac{3}{8}$	$\frac{1}{4}$
$\frac{1}{2}$	$1\frac{3}{16}$	.938	$\frac{7}{16}$	$\frac{5}{16}$
$\frac{9}{16}$	$\frac{7}{8}$	1.010	$\frac{1}{2}$	$1\frac{1}{32}$
$\frac{5}{8}$	1	1.155	$\frac{35}{64}$	$\frac{3}{8}$
$\frac{3}{4}$	$1\frac{1}{8}$	1.299	$2\frac{1}{32}$	$\frac{7}{16}$
$\frac{7}{8}$	$1\frac{5}{16}$	1.516	$4\frac{9}{64}$	$\frac{1}{2}$
1	$1\frac{1}{2}$	1.732	$\frac{7}{8}$	$\frac{9}{16}$
$1\frac{1}{8}$	$1\frac{11}{16}$	1.949	1	$\frac{5}{8}$
$1\frac{1}{4}$	$1\frac{7}{8}$	2.165	$1\frac{3}{32}$	$\frac{3}{4}$
$1\frac{3}{8}$	$2\frac{1}{16}$	2.382	$1\frac{13}{64}$	$1\frac{3}{16}$
$1\frac{1}{2}$	$2\frac{1}{4}$	2.598	$1\frac{5}{16}$	$\frac{7}{8}$

[1] *Abstracted from ASA B18.2—1952*

AMERICAN STANDARD
HEXAGON HEAD CAP SCREWS[1]

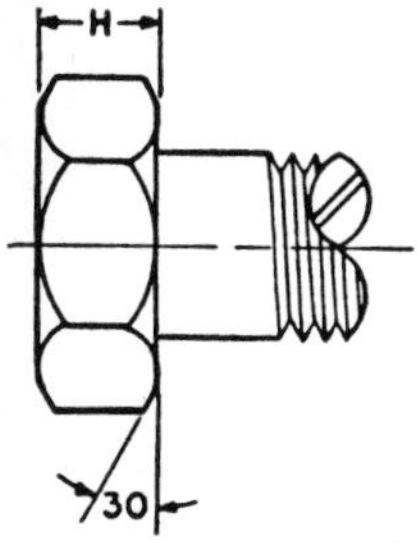

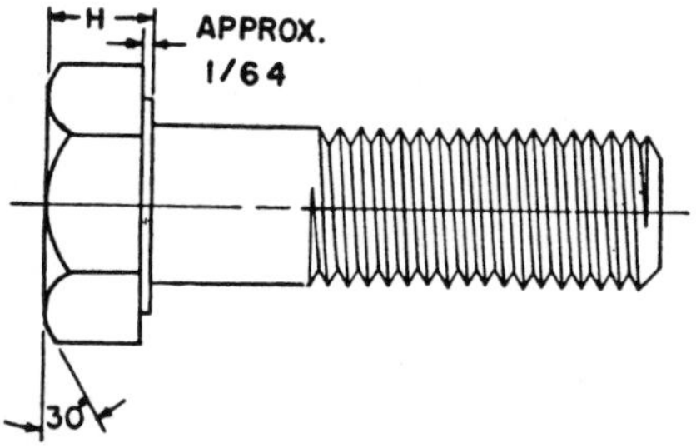

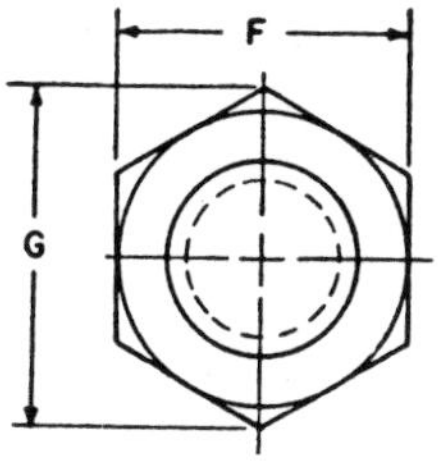

Nominal Size or Basic Major Diameter of Thread	Body Diam. Min. (Maximum Equal to Nom. Size)	Width Across Flats F	Width Across Corners G	Height H
1/4	**.2450**	**7/16**	**.505**	**5/32**
5/16	**.3065**	**1/2**	**.577**	**13/64**
3/8	**.3690**	**9/16**	**.650**	**15/64**
7/16	**.4305**	**5/8**	**.722**	**9/32**
1/2	**.4930**	**3/4**	**.866**	**5/16**
9/16	**.5545**	**13/16**	**.938**	**23/64**
5/8	**.6170**	**15/16**	**1.083**	**25/64**
3/4	**.7410**	**1 1/8**	**1.299**	**15/32**
7/8	**.8660**	**1 5/16**	**1.516**	**35/64**
1	**.9900**	**1 1/2**	**1.732**	**39/64**
1 1/8	1.1140	1 11/16	1.949	11/16
1 1/4	1.2390	1 7/8	2.165	25/32
1 3/8	1.3630	2 1/16	2.382	27/32
1 1/2	1.4880	2 1/4	2.598	15/16

[1] *Abstracted from ASA B18.2—1952*

All dimensions given in inches.

BOLD TYPE INDICATES PRODUCTS UNIFIED DIMENSIONALLY WITH BRITISH AND CANADIAN STANDARDS.

Threads shall be coarse, fine, or 8-thread series, class 2A for plain (unplated) cap screws. For plated cap screws, the diameters may be increased by the amount of class 2A allowance.

AMERICAN STANDARD
FLAT HEAD CAP SCREWS[1]

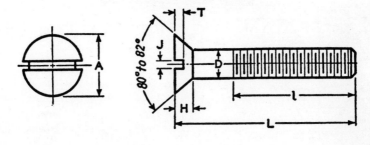

Nominal Size	D	A	H	J	T
	Body Diameter	Head Diameter	Average Height of Head	Width of Slot	Depth of Slot
1/4	.250	.500	.140	.075	.069
5/16	.3125	.625	.176	.084	.086
3/8	.375	.750	.210	.094	.103
7/16	.4375	.8125	.210	.094	.103
1/2	.500	.875	.210	.106	.103
9/16	.5625	1.000	.245	.118	.120
5/8	.625	1.125	.281	.133	.137
3/4	.750	1.375	.352	.149	.171
7/8	.875	1.625	.423	.167	.206
1	1.000	1.875	.494	.188	.240

[1] *Abstracted from ASA B18.6—1947*
All dimensions are given in inches.

AMERICAN STANDARD
FILLISTER HEAD CAP SCREWS[1]

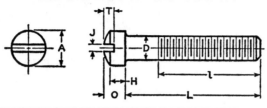

Nominal Size	D	A	H	O	J	T
	Body Diameter	Head Diameter	Height of Head	Total Height of Head	Width of Slot	Depth of Slot
1/4	.250	.375	.172	.216	.075	.097
5/16	.3125	.437	.203	.253	.084	.115
3/8	.375	.562	.250	.314	.094	.143
7/16	.4375	.625	.297	.368	.094	.168
1/2	.500	.750	.328	.412	.106	.188
9/16	.5625	.812	.375	.466	.118	.214
5/8	.625	.875	.422	.521	.133	.240
3/4	.750	1.000	.500	.612	.149	.283
7/8	.875	1.125	.594	.720	.167	.334
1	1.000	1.312	.656	.802	.188	.372

[1] *Abstracted from ASA B18.6—1947*
All dimensions are given in inches.

AMERICAN STANDARD
ROUND HEAD CAP SCREWS[1]

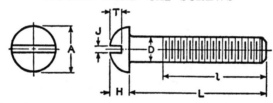

Nominal Size	D	A	H	J	T
	Body Diameter	Head Diameter	Height of Head	Width of Slot	Depth of Slot
1/4	.250	.437	.191	.075	.117
5/16	.3125	.562	.246	.084	.151
3/8	.375	.625	.273	.094	.168
7/16	.4375	.750	.328	.094	.202
1/2	.500	.812	.355	.106	.219
9/16	.5625	.937	.410	.118	.253
5/8	.625	1.000	.438	.133	.270
3/4	.750	1.250	.547	.149	.337

[1] *Abstracted from ASA B18.6—1947*
All dimensions are given in inches.

AMERICAN STANDARD
HEXAGON SOCKET HEAD CAP SCREWS

 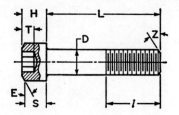

Nominal Size	D Body Diameter	A Head Diameter	H Head Height	S Head Side-Height	J Socket Width Across Flats	Nominal Size	D Body Diameter	A Head Diameter	H Head Height	S Head Side-Height	J Socket Width Across Flats
#1	.0730	.118	.073	.0669	.051	$7/16$	.4375	$5/8$	$7/16$	.4010	.3155
#2	.0860	.140	.086	.0788	.0635	$1/2$	.5000	$3/4$	$1/2$	.4583	.3780
#3	.0990	.161	.099	.0907	.0791	$9/16$	.5625	$13/16$	$9/16$	.5156	.3780
#4	.1120	.183	.112	.1026	.0791	$5/8$	.6250	$7/8$	$5/8$	.5729	.5030
#5	.1250	.205	.125	.1146	.0947	$3/4$	.7500	1	$3/4$	.6875	.5655
#6	.1380	.226	.138	.1265	.0947	$7/8$	.8750	$1 1/8$	$7/8$	.8020	.5655
#8	.1640	.270	.164	.1503	.1270	1	1.0000	$1 5/16$	1	.9166	.6290
#10	.1900	$5/16$	.190	.1741	.1582	$1 1/8$	1.1250	$1 1/2$	$1 1/8$	1.0312	.7540
#12	.2160	$11/32$	.216	.1980	.1582	$1 1/4$	1.2500	$1 3/4$	$1 1/4$	1.1457	.7540
$1/4$	.2500	$3/8$	$1/4$	.2291	.1895	$1 3/8$	1.3750	$1 7/8$	$1 3/8$	1.2604	.7540
$5/16$	.3125	$7/16$	$5/16$	.2864	.2207	$1 1/2$	1.5000	2	$1 1/2$	1.3750	1.0040
$3/8$	.3750	$9/16$	$3/8$	.3437	.3155						

All dimensions in inches.

HEAD CHAMFER (E). The head shall be flat and chamfered. The flat shall be normal to the axis of the screw and the chamfer (E) shall be at an angle of $30° \pm 2°$ with the surface of the flat. The edge between flat and chamfer shall be slightly rounded.

SOCKET DEPTH (T). The depth of socket shall be as great as practicable but varying conditions render it inadvisable to specify definite values for this dimension.

LENGTH UNDER HEAD (L). The length of the screw shall be measured, on a line parallel to the axis, from the plane of the bearing surface under the head to the plane of the flat of the point. The difference between consecutive lengths shall be as follows:

(a) for screw lengths $1/4$ to 1 in., difference = $1/8$ in.
(b) for screw lengths 1 to 4 in., difference = $1/4$ in.
(c) for screw lengths 4 to 6 in., difference = $1/2$ in.

THREAD LENGTH (l). The length of the screw thread is measured from the extreme point to the last usable thread and shall be as follows:

For National Coarse
$\begin{cases} l = 2D + 1/2 \text{ in. (where this length of thread would be greater than half the screw length)} \\ l = 1/2L \text{ (where the length of thread would be greater than } 2D + 1/2 \text{ in.)} \end{cases}$

For National Fine
$\begin{cases} l = 1 1/2 D + 1/2 \text{ in. (where this length of thread would be greater than three-eighths the screw length)} \\ l = 3/8 L \text{ (where this length of thread would be greater than } 1 1/2 D + 1/2 \text{ in.)} \end{cases}$

SCREW POINT CHAMFER (Z). The point shall be flat and chamfered. The flat shall be normal to the axis of the screw and the chamfer (Z) shall be at an angle of $35° + 5°$, $-0°$ with the plane of the flat. The chamfer shall extend to the bottom of the thread and edge between flat and chamfer shall be slightly rounded.

AMERICAN STANDARD
FLAT HEAD MACHINE SCREWS[1]

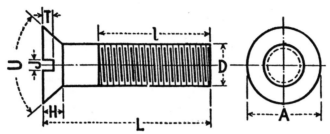

[Countersink angle: Maximum U = 82°; minimum U = 80°]

NOMINAL SIZE	AMERICAN NATIONAL COARSE-THREAD SERIES, CLASS 2 FIT		AMERICAN NATIONAL FINE-THREAD SERIES, CLASS 2 FIT		DIMENSIONS OF HEAD				
					D	A	H	J	T
	Threads per Inch	Body Diameter	Threads per Inch	Body Diameter	Nominal Diameter of Wire	Diameter of Head	Height of Head	Width of Slot	Depth of Slot
0	. . . .	. . . .	80	.0600	. . . .	.119	.030	.022	.015
1	64	.0730	72	.0730	. . . .	.146	.038	.025	.019
2	56	.0860	64	.0860	.086	.172	.046	.036	.023
3	48	.0990	56	.0990	.099	.199	.053	.038	.027
4	40	.1120	48	.1120	.112	.225	.061	.040	.030
5	40	.1250	44	.1250	.125	.252	.069	.043	.034
6	32	.1380	40	.1380	.138	.279	.076	.045	.038
8	32	.1640	36	.1640	.164	.332	.092	.050	.045
10	24	.1900	32	.1900	.190	.385	.107	.055	.053
12	24	.2160	28	.2160	.216	.438	.122	.059	.060
1/4	20	.2500	28	.2500	.250	.507	.142	.066	.070
5/16	18	.3125	24	.3125	.3125	.636	.179	.077	.088
3/8	16	.3750	24	.3750	.3750	.762	.215	.088	.106
7/16	14	.4375	20	.4375	.4375	.813	.220	.098	.110
1/2	13	.5000	20	.5000	.5000	.875	.220	.110	.110
9/16	12	.5625	18	.5625	.5625	1.000	.256	.123	.128
5/8	11	.6250	18	.6250	.6250	1.125	.293	.138	.146
3/4	10	.7500	16	.7500	.7500	1.375	.366	.154	.183

[1] *Abstracted from H28, National Bureau of Standards*

AMERICAN STANDARD
ROUND HEAD MACHINE SCREWS[1]

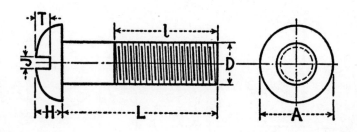

NOMINAL SIZE	AMERICAN NATIONAL COARSE-THREAD SERIES, CLASS 2 FIT		AMERICAN NATIONAL FINE-THREAD SERIES, CLASS 2 FIT		DIMENSIONS OF HEAD				
					D	*A*	*H*	*J*	*T*
	Threads per Inch	Body Diameter	Threads per Inch	Body Diameter	Nominal Diameter of Wire	Diameter of Head	Height of Head	Width of Slot	Depth of Slot
0	. . . . . .	. . . . . .	80	.0600	.060	.113	.053	.022	.039
1	64	.0730	72	.0730	.073	.138	.061	.025	.043
2	56	.0860	64	.0860	.086	.162	.070	.036	.048
3	48	.0990	56	.0990	.099	.187	.078	.038	.053
4	40	.1120	48	.1120	.112	.211	.086	.040	.058
5	40	.1250	44	.1250	.125	.236	.095	.043	.062
6	32	.1380	40	.1380	.138	.260	.103	.045	.067
8	32	.1640	36	.1640	.164	.309	.119	.050	.076
10	24	.1900	32	.1900	.190	.359	.136	.055	.086
12	24	.2160	28	.2160	.216	.408	.152	.059	.095
¼	20	.2500	28	.2500	.250	.472	.174	.066	.108
⁵⁄₁₆	18	.3125	24	.3125	.3125	.591	.214	.077	.130
³⁄₈	16	.3750	24	.3750	.3750	.708	.254	.088	.153
⁷⁄₁₆	14	.4375	20	.4375	.4375	.750	.328	.098	.202
½	13	.5000	20	.5000	.5000	.813	.355	.110	.219
⁹⁄₁₆	12	.5625	18	.5625	.5625	.938	.410	.123	.253
⅝	11	.6250	18	.6250	.6250	1.000	.438	.138	.270
¾	10	.7500	16	.7500	.7500	1.250	.547	.154	.337

[1] *Abstracted from H28, National Bureau of Standards*

AMERICAN STANDARD OVAL HEAD MACHINE SCREWS[1]

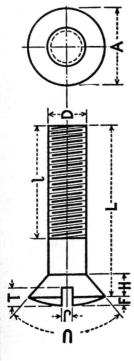

[Countersink angle: Maximum $\theta = 82°$; minimum $\theta = 80°$]

NOMINAL SIZE	AMERICAN NATIONAL COARSE-THREAD SERIES, CLASS 2 FIT		AMERICAN NATIONAL FINE-THREAD SERIES, CLASS 2 FIT		DIMENSIONS OF HEAD						
	Threads per Inch	Body Diameter, Maximum	Threads per Inch	Body Diameter, Maximum	D — Nominal Diameter of Wire	A — Diameter of Head	H — Height of Head, Nominal	J — Width of Slot	T — Depth of Slot	F — Height of Oval	F and H — Total Height of Head
0	......	......	80	.0600	.060	.119	.030	.022	.030	.021	.056
1	64	.0730	72	.0730	.073	.146	.038	.025	.038	.025	.068
2	56	.0860	64	.0860	.086	.172	.046	.036	.045	.029	.080
3	48	.0990	56	.0990	.099	.199	.053	.038	.052	.033	.092
4	40	.1120	48	.1120	.112	.225	.061	.040	.059	.037	.104
5	40	.1250	44	.1250	.125	.252	.069	.043	.067	.041	.116
6	32	.1380	40	.1380	.138	.279	.076	.045	.074	.045	.128
8	32	.1640	36	.1640	.164	.332	.092	.050	.088	.053	.152
10	24	.1900	32	.1900	.190	.385	.107	.055	.103	.061	.176
12	24	.2160	28	.2160	.216	.438	.122	.059	.117	.069	.200
1/4	20	.2500	28	.2500	.250	.507	.142	.066	.136	.079	.232
5/16	18	.3125	24	.3125	.3125	.636	.179	.077	.171	.098	.290
3/8	16	.3750	24	.3750	.3750	.762	.215	.088	.206	.117	.347
7/16	14	.4375	20	.4375	.4375	.813	.220	.098	.209	.125	.355
1/2	13	.5000	20	.5000	.5000	.875	.220	.110	.214	.135	.365

[1] Abstracted from H28, National Bureau of Standards

AMERICAN STANDARD FILLISTER HEAD MACHINE SCREWS[1]

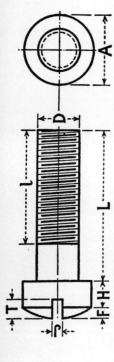

NOMINAL SIZE	AMERICAN NATIONAL COARSE-THREAD SERIES, CLASS 2 FIT		AMERICAN NATIONAL FINE-THREAD SERIES, CLASS 2 FIT		DIMENSIONS OF HEAD						
	Threads per Inch	Body Diameter	Threads per Inch	Body Diameter	D Nominal Diameter of Wire	A Diameter of Head	H Height of Head	J Width of Slot	T Depth of Slot	F Height of Oval	F and H Total Height of Head
0	....	....	80	.0600	.060	.096	.045	.022	.025	.014	.059
1	64	.0730	72	.0730	.073	.118	.053	.025	.031	.017	.070
2	56	.0860	64	.0860	.086	.140	.055	.036	.037	.028	.083
3	48	.0990	56	.0990	.099	.161	.063	.038	.043	.032	.095
4	40	.1120	48	.1120	.112	.183	.072	.040	.048	.035	.107
5	40	.1250	44	.1250	.125	.205	.081	.043	.054	.039	.120
6	32	.1380	40	.1380	.138	.226	.089	.045	.060	.043	.132
8	32	.1640	36	.1640	.164	.270	.106	.050	.071	.050	.156
10	24	.1900	32	.1900	.190	.313	.123	.055	.083	.057	.180
12	24	.2160	28	.2160	.216	.357	.141	.059	.094	.064	.205
1/4	20	.2500	28	.2500	.250	.414	.163	.066	.109	.074	.237
5/16	18	.3125	24	.3125	.3125	.519	.205	.077	.137	.092	.297
3/8	16	.3750	24	.3750	.3750	.622	.246	.088	.164	.109	.355
7/16	14	.4375	20	.4375	.4375	.625	.297	.098	.168	.071	.368
1/2	13	.5000	20	.5000	.5000	.750	.328	.110	.188	.084	.412
9/16	12	.5625	18	.5625	.5625	.812	.375	.123	.214	.091	.466
5/8	11	.6250	18	.6250	.6250	.875	.422	.138	.240	.099	.521
3/4	10	.7500	16	.7500	.7500	1.000	.500	.154	.283	.112	.612
7/8	9	.8750	14	.8750	.8750	1.125	.594	.173	.334	.126	.720
1	8	1.0000	14	1.0000	1.0000	1.312	.656	.194	.372	.146	.802

[1] Abstracted from H28, National Bureau of Standards

AMERICAN STANDARD
SQUARE HEAD SET SCREWS[1]

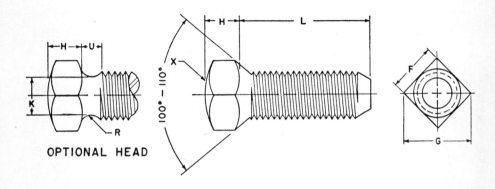

OPTIONAL HEAD

Nominal Size		Width Across Flats F	Width Across Corners G	Height of Head H	Diameter of Neck Relief K	Radius of Head X	Radius of Neck Relief R	Width of Neck Relief U
# 10	.190	.1875	.247	$9/64$	.145	$15/32$	.027	.083
# 12	.216	.216	.292	$5/32$	.162	$35/64$	.029	.091
1/4	.250	.250	.331	$3/16$	.185	$5/8$	.032	.100
5/16	.3125	.3125	.415	$15/64$	.240	$25/32$	.036	.111
3/8	.3750	.375	.497	$9/32$	.294	$15/16$	.041	.125
7/16	.4375	.4375	.581	$21/64$	.345	$1\ 3/32$	.046	.143
1/2	.500	.500	.665	$3/8$	.400	$1\ 1/4$	.050	.154
9/16	.5625	.5625	.748	$27/64$	.454	$1\ 13/32$	.054	.167
5/8	.6250	.625	.833	$15/32$	.507	$1\ 9/16$	.059	.182
3/4	.750	.750	1.001	$9/16$	.620	$1\ 7/8$	.065	.200
7/8	.875	.875	1.170	$21/32$	.731	$2\ 3/16$	.072	.222
1	1.000	1.000	1.337	$3/4$	.838	$2\ 1/2$	.081	.250
1 1/8	1.125	1.125	1.505	$27/32$	.939	$2\ 13/16$	.092	.283
1 1/4	1.250	1.250	1.674	$15/16$	1.064	$3\ 1/8$	.092	.283
1 3/8	1.375	1.375	1.843	$1\ 1/32$	1.159	$3\ 7/16$	.109	.333
1 1/2	1.500	1.500	2.010	$1\ 1/8$	1.284	$3\ 3/4$	.109	.333

[1] *Abstracted from ASA B18.2—1952*
All dimensions given in inches.

AMERICAN STANDARD
STEEL WOOD SCREWS

Screw Size	Dia.	s	Round Head			Flat Head			Countersunk Oval Head			
			a	b	c	a	b	c	a	b	c	d
2	.086	.033	.146 .162	.059 .070	.036 .048	.156 .172	.051	.015 .023	.156 .172	.051	.037 .045	.063 .080
3	.099	.035	.169 .187	.067 .078	.040 .053	.181 .199	.059	.017 .027	.181 .199	.059	.043 .052	.073 .092
4	.112	.037	.193 .211	.075 .086	.043 .058	.207 .225	.067	.020 .030	.207 .225	.067	.049 .059	.084 .104
5	.125	.040	.217 .236	.083 .095	.047 .062	.232 .252	.075	.022 .034	.232 .252	.075	.055 .067	.095 .116
6	.138	.042	.240 .260	.091 .103	.050 .067	.257 .279	.083	.024 .038	.257 .279	.083	.060 .074	.105 .128
7	.151	.042	.264 .285	.099 .111	.053 .072	.283 .305	.091	.027 .041	.283 .305	.091	.066 .081	.116 .140
8	.164	.047	.287 .309	.107 .119	.057 .076	.308 .332	.100	.029 .045	.308 .332	.100	.072 .088	.126 .152
9	.177	.047	.311 .334	.115 .128	.060 .081	.334 .358	.108	.032 .049	.334 .358	.108	.078 .095	.137 .164
10	.190	.052	.334 .359	.124 .136	.064 .086	.359 .385	.116	.034 .053	.359 .385	.116	.084 .103	.148 .176
12	.216	.056	.382 .408	.140 .152	.071 .095	.410 .438	.132	.039 .060	.410 .438	.132	.096 .117	.169 .200
14	.242	.060	.429 .457	.156 .169	.078 .105	.461 .491	.148	.044 .068	.461 .491	.148	.108 .132	.190 .224
16	.268	.063	.476 .506	.172 .185	.085 .114	.512 .544	.164	.049 .075	.512 .544	.164	.120 .146	.212 .248
18	.294	.067	.523 .555	.188 .202	.092 .123	.563 .597	.180	.054 .083	.563 .597	.180	.132 .160	.233 .272

WOODRUFF KEYS

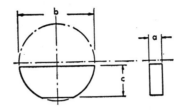

KEY NUMBER	(a) Width of Key	(b) Diameter of Key	(c) Height of Key	Size
204	.0635	.500	.203	$\frac{1}{16}$ x $\frac{1}{2}$
304	.0948	.500	.203	$\frac{3}{32}$ x $\frac{1}{2}$
305	.0948	.625	.250	$\frac{3}{32}$ x $\frac{5}{8}$
404	.1260	.500	.203	$\frac{1}{8}$ x $\frac{1}{2}$
405	.1260	.625	.250	$\frac{1}{8}$ x $\frac{5}{8}$
406	.1260	.750	.313	$\frac{1}{8}$ x $\frac{3}{4}$
505	.1573	.625	.250	$\frac{5}{32}$ x $\frac{5}{8}$
506	.1573	.750	.313	$\frac{5}{32}$ x $\frac{3}{4}$
507	.1573	.875	.375	$\frac{5}{32}$ x $\frac{7}{8}$
606	.1885	.750	.313	$\frac{3}{16}$ x $\frac{3}{4}$
607	.1885	.875	.375	$\frac{3}{16}$ x $\frac{7}{8}$
608	.1885	1.000	.438	$\frac{3}{16}$ x 1
609	.1885	1.125	.484	$\frac{3}{16}$ x $1\frac{1}{8}$
807	.2510	.875	.375	$\frac{1}{4}$ x $\frac{7}{8}$
808	.2510	1.000	.438	$\frac{1}{4}$ x 1
809	.2510	1.125	.484	$\frac{1}{4}$ x $1\frac{1}{8}$
810	.2510	1.250	.547	$\frac{1}{4}$ x $1\frac{1}{4}$
811	.2510	1.375	.594	$\frac{1}{4}$ x $1\frac{3}{8}$
812	.2510	1.500	.641	$\frac{1}{4}$ x $1\frac{1}{2}$
1008	.3135	1.000	.438	$\frac{5}{16}$ x 1
1009	.3135	1.125	.484	$\frac{5}{16}$ x $1\frac{1}{8}$
1010	.3135	1.250	.547	$\frac{5}{16}$ x $1\frac{1}{4}$
1011	.3135	1.375	.594	$\frac{5}{16}$ x $1\frac{3}{8}$
1012	.3135	1.500	.641	$\frac{5}{16}$ x $1\frac{1}{2}$
1210	.3760	1.250	.547	$\frac{3}{8}$ x $1\frac{1}{4}$
1211	.3760	1.375	.594	$\frac{3}{8}$ x $1\frac{3}{8}$
1212	.3760	1.500	.641	$\frac{3}{8}$ x $1\frac{1}{2}$

INDEX

PAGE

A

Acme thread 118
Alphabet of lines 31, 32
American standard threads ..115–116
American Welding Society 129
Ames lettering triangle 58
Angles
  bisecting 37
  construction 25
  dimensioning 68
Appliance circuit diagrams 215
Architect 10
Architect's scale 20–21
Architectural drafting 10–11, 179–191
Arcs
  bisecting 36
  construction 25–26
  dimensioning 67–68
  tangent 37–39
Arrowheads 65
Artistic sketches 4
Assembly drawing 75, 111–115
  diagram 111
  dimensioning 112
  identification of parts 112
  outline 111, 112
  unit 111–112
  working 111–112
Auxiliary views 103–107
  construction 104–107
  types 103–104

PAGE

B

Bar graph 219
Base line dimensioning 68–69
Bill of material 112, 115
Bisecting
  angle 37
  arc 36
  line 36
Blueprint 229–233
  history 229–230
  machine 232–233
  making 230–232
  sunframe 231
Black and white prints 229, 235
Board, drafting 17
Bolts 119–121, 123–124
Bolts, sections through 96
Bottom view 76, 78
Braddock-Rowe lettering trian-
  gle 57–58
Break line 32
Broken-out sectional view 93–94
Building terms 180, 181
Buttress thread 118

C

Cabinet drawing 159
Cap screws 122–123
Carriage bolts 123–124
Center line 32
Charts 219–224
Circles 25–26, 29, 67–68, 173

PAGE

Civil engineer's scale 23
Coarseness of thread 116–117
Compass 25, 26
Composition in lettering 56
Constructing auxiliary views 105–107
Construction line 23
Conventional screw threads ..118–119
Cross section paper 171–172
Cross section views 91–97
Curved surfaces 81
Curves
   irregular 29
   isometric 157
Cutting plane lines 32, 92
Cylindrical development 140, 142–146

D

Designers 4, 11–14
Detail drawing 75
Developments 139–148
   cylinder 140, 142–146
   radial 140–142
   square and rectangular ...140, 147
   transition pieces 148
Dimensioning 65–71, 112–113
   angles 68
   arcs 67–68
   assembly drawings 112
   base line 68–69
   bolts 121–122, 123–124
   circles 67–68
   curves 67–68
   fillets 67–68
   guide lines 67
   holes 67–68
   piping drawings 207
   placement 65–67
   rules for 66–68
   staggered 66

PAGE

Dimensioning—*continued*
   surface finish 70–71
   tabular 112
   threads 118–125
Dimension lines 32, 66–68
Dividing a line 28, 36–37
Dividers 27
   types 27
   use 28
Drafting 1–16
   architectural 10
   fields 9
   importance 3–6
   industrial 9
   lines 31, 32
   machine 30
   military service 15
   paper 30, 31
   template 29, 30
   topographical 14
Drafting board 17
Drafting sheet 31, 33
   laying out 33, 45–48
   size 31
Draftsquare 29
Drawing
   arcs 25, 26, 29, 37–39
   assembly 75, 111–115
   border lines 33
   circles 25, 26, 29, 48, 158
   constructions 36–40
   diagram assembly 111, 114
   electrical 210–216
   freehand 171–175
   graphs and charts 219–225
   heating 209–210
   horizontal lines 23–24, 173
   irregular lines 29, 157
   lettering 53–58

PAGE

Drawing—*continued*
  outline assembly 112
  pattern 139–148
  pictorial 114, 155–166
  piping 198–208
  schematic 197, 214
  slanted lines 23–24, 94–95
  title strip 33–34
  to scale 22
  vertical lines 23–24
  working assembly 75, 112
Drawing tangent arcs 37–39

E

Electrical drawings 114, 210–216
Electrical wiring symbols 213
Electrical terms 210–214
Ellipse 40
End view 76–80
Engineering drafting 15
Engineer's scale 23
Enlarged drawings 21, 94
Erasing pencil marks 34–35
Erasing procedure 34–35
Erasing shield 34–35
Exploded assembly 113, 114
Extension line 32, 65

F

Fasteners 115–129
Fields of drafting 9
Fillets and rounds 69–70, 82
Financing a home 187
Fine threads 116
Finish marks 70–71
Fits of threads 117
Flat key 125
Floor plans 189–191, 214
Forming letters 54–56

PAGE

Flow charts 221, 224
Fractions 66
Freehand sketching 4, 171–175
French curves 29
Front view 76–80, 158–159
Full sectional view 92, 93

G

Geometric constructions 23–29, 36–40
Gothic alphabet 54
Graphs 219–224
  area 224
  bar 222–223
  line 219–222
Guide lines for lettering 56–57

H

Half sectional view 93
Heating
  drawings 209–210
  symbols 210
  systems 209
Hexagon 39
Hidden
  lines 32, 80–81, 112
  surfaces 80–81
Hole template 29
Home planning 179–190
  determining cost 187–189
  determining size 187–189
  financing 187
  securing a lot 186
  sketching floor plan 189–191
Horizon line 160
House architecture 181–186
  Cape Cod 185
  Dutch Colonial 184
  Elizabethan 183
  English 182
  Georgian 184

House architecture—*continued*
Modernistic 182
Regency 185
Southern Colonial 184
Spanish 185–186
traditional 182–186

I

Inch and foot symbols 66
Inclined lettering 54–55
Industrial designer 13
Industrial design service 13
Industrial draftsman 9
Intersections 142–147
Irregular curve 29
Isometric circle 158
Isometric drawing 155–158

J

Jam nut 128
Joints, welded 129

K

Keys, specifications for 125
Knuckle thread 118

L

Layout 45–48, 139–148
drawing 33, 45–48, 139–148
squared-paper 48
Leaders 68
Left-hand thread 117
Lettering 53–58
devices 57–58
forming 54–56
guide lines 56–57
pencil 18, 58
spacing 56
strokes 54–56
types 53–54
width 54–55
Line graph 219–222

Lines
bisecting 36
border 33
break 32
center 32
construction 33
cutting plane 32, 92
dimension 32
dividing 28
extension 32
freehand 172–173
guide lines 56–57
hidden 32, 80–81
object 32
section 32, 92–96
Locking devices 127–128
Lofting 47

M

Machine screws 123
Mechanical engineer's scale 22
Measuring scales 20–23
Military service 15
Multiple threads 117

N

Nails 127
National Coarse thread 116
National Fine thread 116
Nonisometric lines 156–158
Notes 57, 69
Numbers of views 76–78
Numerals 55
Nuts 119–121, 124, 127–128

O

Object line 32
Oblique drawing 155, 158–159
Occupational opportunities 9–15
One-view drawing 47–48
Outline assembly drawing ..111, 112
Ozalid prints 229, 234

P

Paper
blueprint 230
cross section 48, 171–172
drawing 30–31
fastening 33
Ozalid 234
sizes 31
Partial auxiliary view 104–105
Parts list 112, 115
Pattern drawing 139–148
cylindrical 140, 142–146
radial 140–142
rectangular 140, 147
square 140, 147
Pencil 18, 58, 172
grade 18, 58
markings 18, 58
points 18, 58
sharpening 18, 19, 58
Pentagon 39
Perspective drawing 155, 159–162
Pictorial drawings 114, 155–166
cabinet 159
isometric 154–158
oblique 155, 158–159
perspective 155, 159–162
Pie graph 224
Pins, sections through 96
Pipe 198–208
fittings 201–202
kinds 199
Pipe thread 118
Piping and tubing 198–200
Piping drawings 198–208
Piping symbols 202, 204–205
Pitch of thread 117
Placement of views ..75–77, 105–107
Planning a home 179–191

PAGE

Plumbing 200–201
Prints
black and white 229, 235
blue 230–233
duplicating tracing 235
Ozalid 229, 234
Van Dyke 229, 233
Projection 76–80, 105–107
Projection of views ..76–80, 105–107
Protractor
description 25
use 25

R

Radial development 140–142
Radio symbols 215
Ranch house 182
Rectangular pattern 140, 147
Reference line 106
Representing sectional views ..94–95
Reproduction of drawings ..229–235
Revolved sectional views 91, 94
Ribs, sections through 96
Rivets 125–127
Rounded corners 68–69, 81–82
Rules for dimensioning 66–68

S

Sandpaper pad 19
Scale drawings 22
Scale guard 20
Scales 20–23
architect's 20–21
engineer's 22–23
Schematic drawings 197–216
Screw thread 115–119
Acme 118
American Standard 115, 116
buttress 118
fits 117
knuckle 118

PAGE

Screw thread—*continued*
lead 116
left-hand 117
multiple 117
pipe 118
pitch 116–117
representation 118, 119
single 117
square 118
symbols 119
terminology 116
Unified 116
Screws
cap 122–123
machine 123
self-tapping 125
set 122
wood 124–125
Securing a lot 186
Section line 32, 92–96
Sectional views 91–96, 158
bolts 96
broken-out 93–94
full 92
half 93
isometric 158
pins 96
revolved 91, 94
ribs 96
shafts 96
symbols 95–96
webs 96
Self-tapping screws 125
Set screw 122
Shaded areas, location of 162–165
Shading 162–166
broad stroke and smudge ..165–166
line 163–165
stippling 165

PAGE

Shafts, sections through 96
Sharpening pencil 18, 19
Ship curve 29
Sideview 76
Single thread 117
Sketching 171–175, 189–191
circles 173
floor plan 189–191
pencil 172
pictorial drawing 175
straight lines 173
type of lines 172–173
working drawing 173–174
Spacing letters 56
Square key 125
Square pattern 140, 147
Square thread 118
Standard breaks 96
Stove bolts 123
Studs 121–122
Sunframe 231
Surfaces
curved 81
hidden 80–81
Symbols
architectural 190
electrical 213
heating and ventilating 210
materials 95–96
piping 202, 204–205
radio 215
thread 119
welding 128–129

T

Tabular dimensions 104
Tangent arcs 37–39
Template 29–30

Thread pitch 117
Threaded fasteners 115–125
    bolt 119–121, 123–124
    cap screw 122–123
    carriage bolts 123–124
    machine screw 123
    self-tapping screws 125
    set screw 122
    stove bolts 123
    studs 121–122
    wood screws 124–125
Threads 115–119
    Acme 118
    American Standard 115–116
    buttress 118
    coarseness 116–117
    fits 117
    how designated 117–119
    knuckle 118
    National 116
    National coarse 116
    National fine 116
    pipe 118
    pitch 109, 111, 117, 119
    square 118
    symbols 119
    Unified standard 116
Three-view drawings 75–80
Title strip 33–34
Tolerance 70
Tool designer 14
Topographical drafting 14, 15
Top view 76–80
Tracing cloth 30
Tracing paper 30
Triangles 23
Triangular scale 20–23
T-square 23
Two-view drawings 75, 77–78

U

Unified standard thread 116
Uniformity of lettering 54–57
Unit assembly drawing 111–112

V

Valves 202–203
Vanishing point 160
Van Dyke prints 229, 230
Ventilating symbols 210
Vertical letters 54–55
Views 76–80
    Auxiliary 103–107
    blocking in 77
    bottom 76–78
    broken-out 93–94
    choice 75–78
    end 76–78
    front 76–78
    meaning 76
    number 76–78
    placement 75–77, 105–107
    projection 78–80
    representing 76–80
    revolved 91, 94
    sectional 91–96, 158
    side 76
    top 76–80
V-thread 115–116

W

Washers 127–128
Webs, sections through 96
Welding 128–129
    joints 128–129
    symbols 128–129
Woodruff key 125
Wood screws 124–125
Working assembly drawing ..75, 112
Working drawing ...75–82, 173–175

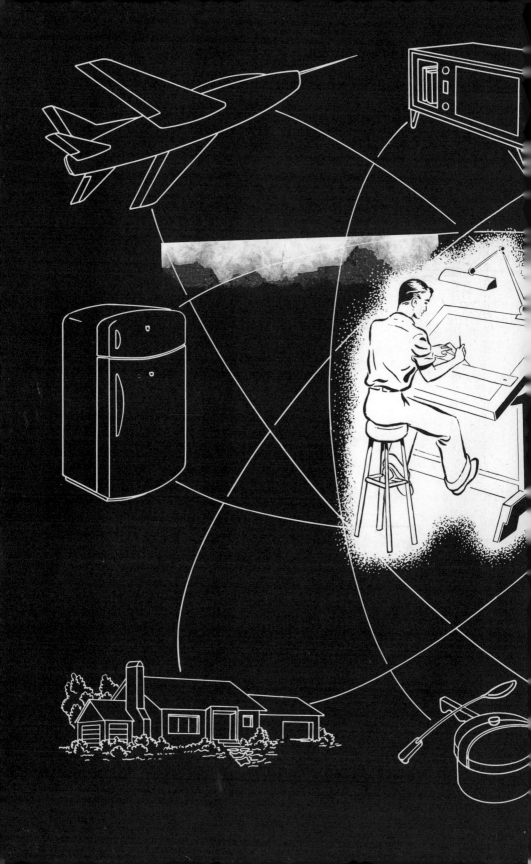